student WORKBOOK

GCSE History
Germany, 1918–45

Nick Dyer & Geoff Layton

Philip Allan Updates, part of the Hodder Education Group, an Hachette Livre UK company, Market Place, Deddington, Oxfordshire OX15 0SE

Orders
Bookpoint Ltd, 130 Milton Park, Abingdon, Oxfordshire OX14 4SB
tel: 01235 827720, fax: 01235 400454
e-mail: uk.orders@bookpoint.co.uk
Lines are open 9.00 a.m.–5.00 p.m., Monday to Saturday, with a 24-hour message answering service. You can also order through the Philip Allan Updates website: www.philipallan.co.uk

© Philip Allan Updates 2007

ISBN 978-1-84489-139-9

Printed in Spain

Philip Allan Updates' policy is to use papers that are natural, renewable and recyclable products and made from wood grown in sustainable forests. The logging and manufacturing processes are expected to conform to the environmental regulations of the country of origin.

Introduction

This workbook is designed to help you prepare for the Germany option of your GCSE Modern World History course. It covers the requirements of the following examination boards:

- OCR History B. Germany, 1919–45
- AQA Specification B. Germany, 1919–39
- Edexcel History A. Germany, 1930–39

The content is divided into seven topics, each of which provides an overview of an important aspect of German history from 1918 to 1945.

Each topic aims to:

- strengthen both your **knowledge** and **understanding** of the period
- test your ability to **explain** and **communicate** your responses clearly and precisely
- help you develop your ability to **analyse** and **evaluate** sources

The notes in this workbook should be used in conjunction with your class notes and textbooks. This will enable you to provide comprehensive and effective answers that will be helpful when you come to revise for the exam.

The questions test your ability to:

- define terms and concepts
- use source material critically to answer questions
- complete a partially filled table
- write short-answer responses
- label diagrams and tables
- write extended answers, based on exam-type questions

Space is provided for your answers — the line allocation given to each question indicates how much you should be aiming to write for your answer. The final question in most topics gives you the opportunity for **extended writing** and should therefore be answered on separate sheets of paper.

Key question

Was the Weimar Republic doomed from the start?

 Key content

- The German Revolution and the birth of the Weimar Republic, 1918–19
- Armistice and the effects of the Treaty of Versailles
- Weimar's weaknesses
- The economic crisis: hyperinflation and the Ruhr occupation

The German Revolution and the birth of the Weimar Republic, 1918–19

 How did Germany emerge from defeat in the First World War?

The November revolution

By autumn 1918 Germany was facing the threat of military defeat and invasion. The German military offensive of spring 1918 had failed to give victory and in the summer Germany's other allies, Austria-Hungary, Turkey and Bulgaria, were collapsing.

Moreover, there were signs of increasing distress for the German people, which was partly caused by the British naval blockade imposed since 1914:

- a growing number of strikes in factories
- shortages of vital goods, e.g. coal and grain
- a decline in workers' 'real wages' as inflation increased
- the human upset of war — 2.4 million German dead and many disabled soldiers

Therefore, in September 1918 Germany's generals, led by Hindenburg and Ludendorff, were so frightened by the threat of military defeat and invasion that they decided to bring about political changes. Their general aim was to reduce the powers of the Kaiser, Emperor Wilhelm II, and to give more authority to the Reichstag, the German parliament. They hoped this would:

- prevent Germany collapsing into communist revolution
- gain more sympathy from the Allies in order to get better peace terms based on Wilson's 14 Points. (This was a proposal made by the American president, Woodrow Wilson, in January 1918 aimed at ending the war.)

Communism and socialism in Europe

At the beginning of the twentieth century the ideas of communism and socialism based on the writings of Karl Marx were growing in popularity across Europe among workers and trade unions. But, surprisingly, the first communist revolution took place in Russia in November 1917, when the Bolshevik Party, led by Lenin and Trotsky, had seized power.

The country with the largest socialist movement was Germany, but by the end of the war it was deeply divided. On the one hand, there was a small group of communists called the Spartacists, led by Liebknecht and Luxemburg, who wanted to spread a revolution to Germany, like the Bolsheviks in Russia. On the other hand, the majority of socialists, led by Ebert, were more cautious and supported the establishment of a democratic parliament (see Table 1 on page 4).

Table 1   The socialist movement in Germany

Party name	Social Democratic Party (SPD)	Spartacus League, which became the Communist Party (KPD)
Aims	To create a socialist Germany, but committed to parliamentary democracy	To seize power and create a communist state
Leaders and supporters in 1918	Friedrich Ebert and the moderate socialists	Rosa Luxemburg, Karl Liebknecht and the revolutionary socialists
Main features	The largest party in the Reichstag	Formed in 1916 to oppose the war; encouraged by Russian Bolsheviks; 5,000 members

On 3 October 1918 Prince Max von Baden was appointed (with the Kaiser's agreement) as the chancellor of a coalition government. However, in the next few weeks there was no fundamental improvement in Germany's military and domestic situation. Unrest came to a head quickly, resulting in the November revolution. The developments outlined in Table 2 were crucial.

Ebert's provisional government

On 9 November 1918 Ebert created a provisional coalition government. It was 'provisional' because it was only to continue in office until a national election was held to vote for

Table 2   Events of the November revolution in Germany

29 October ⇩	**Naval mutiny** Sailors refused military orders at Wilhelmshaven. The mutiny spread quickly and by 2 November sailors gained control of other ports such as Kiel and Hamburg.
6 November ⇩	**Riots start** Disturbances in major cities, such as Cologne and Berlin.
9 November ⇩	**Declaration of a German republic** In the difficult situation the prince handed the chancellorship over to Friedrich Ebert, the leader of the Social Democrats. **Abdication of the Kaiser** Under pressure from his generals Wilhelm II agreed to abdicate and went into exile in Holland.
11 November	**The armistice** The representatives of Germany and the Allies signed the Armistice to end the fighting, but the peace terms were not agreed until the signing of the Treaty of Versailles (see pages 6–7).

a new democratic Reichstag (parliament). It was a 'coalition' because it was a combination of parties, the SPD and some others.

This new government faced great problems in Germany in various areas:

- **Economic**. There were basic shortages of food and fuel, and inflation was increasing.
- **Social**. There were serious health problems, such as flu and hypothermia.
- **Military**. Millions of troops were being demobilised and a peace treaty was needed.
- **Political**. The government faced opposition from both sides. The left wing (e.g. the **Spartacists**) aimed for a more revolutionary policy. The right wing (e.g. the **generals and landowners**) were bitter at the military defeat and the abdication of the Kaiser.

Chancellor Ebert was a moderate and he was frightened that the political situation in Germany could run out of control. He was particularly worried that the return of troops could lead to communist-style revolution. In this difficult position, a significant decision was made on the telephone on 10 November 1918. In what has become known as the **Ebert–Groener agreement**, General Groener agreed to back the new government and to maintain law and order. In return, Ebert agreed to resist communism and to uphold the authority of the army, the judges and the civil service. As a result, from that time, these traditional forces had great power in the new republic.

Despite all these problems in Germany, in the winter of 1918–19 the first proper democratic national election was held. It took place on 19 January 1919 and in February the Reichstag was opened at the town of Weimar. Ebert was chosen as president and Scheidemann was invited to form a coalition of the SPD and other democratic parties.

The Weimar Constitution

Following a national election the new parliament met at the town of Weimar and a constitution was drawn up and agreed in August 1919. The main features were:
- German citizens had many individual rights, e.g. freedom of speech and religion.
- German citizens were also provided with a range of social rights, e.g. welfare care.
- The president was to be elected by the people every 7 years, and had considerable powers such as:
  - the right to dissolve the Reichstag
  - the appointment of the chancellor, who was responsible for day-to-day government
  - the right to rule in a national emergency (Article 48) by using decrees, i.e. laws created without the use of parliament
- The Reichstag was the main law-making body of the parliament. It consisted of deputies elected every 4 years using a system of **proportional representation**. (This system of voting gives seats in a parliament in proportion to the total number of votes.)

The Armistice and the Treaty of Versailles

 What was the impact of the Treaty of Versailles on the Republic?

Although the Kaiser and his generals had run Germany during the First World War, it was Ebert and other Weimar politicians who soon became associated with the loss of the war. This may have been because Ebert had made the decision to sign the Armistice on 11 November 1918. From that time, the opponents of democracy (e.g. nationalists on the right wing) created the myth that Germany had been betrayed by the so-called **November criminals** who had 'stabbed the German Army in the back'.

However, when the news of the terms of the Treaty of Versailles (see Figure 1 on page 7) was released in June 1919, there was genuine shock and outrage among the German public. Most Germans thought the treaty unjust and humiliating because:

- It was **not negotiated**, but was imposed on Germany by the Allies: it was called a ***Diktat*** — a dictated peace.
- The **War Guilt Clause (Article 231)** placed the blame and the responsibility on Germany for starting the war and for all the damage.
- It forced Germany to sign a 'blank cheque' for the **reparations**. Germany had to agree to pay reparations, although the final sum was not agreed until the Reparations Commission was to make its decision in 1921.
- It **disarmed Germany**, while Britain and France remained highly armed.
- It meant that Germany **lost territories** including German-living areas, e.g. Austria, Danzig and the 'Polish corridor'.
- It did not even allow Germany to join the **League of Nations**.

Of course, the Allies felt that the treaty was quite reasonable. In fact, the French complained that it was not harsh enough. However, virtually all Germans believed the treaty was

humiliating and vindictive and could not be accepted. Most significantly, the new democratic Weimar government was increasingly blamed for signing it. As a result, the 'stab-in-the-back myth' and the Treaty of Versailles became an easy explanation for all Germany's problems.

Weimar's weaknesses

 Why was there so much disorder in Germany 1919–23?

From the start, President Ebert and the Weimar governments faced opposition from both the extreme left and the extreme right.

The Spartacist uprising

The Spartacists, who were later renamed the **Communist Party (KPD)**, launched an armed uprising in January 1919 in Berlin. Their aim was to bring about a communist revolution in Germany (like Russia) and to establish a communist state. However, the uprising was crushed quite easily by army troops, along with the help of some anti-communist units known as the ***Freikorps***. In Berlin over 100 workers were killed (including the Spartacist leaders, Liebknecht and Luxemburg).

Over the next few years there was a range of left-wing disturbances across Germany. The most significant were:

- the declaration of a Soviet republic in Bavaria in March 1919
- a communist uprising in the Ruhr in March 1920
- a broader uprising in 1923 which became known as the 'German October' in Saxony

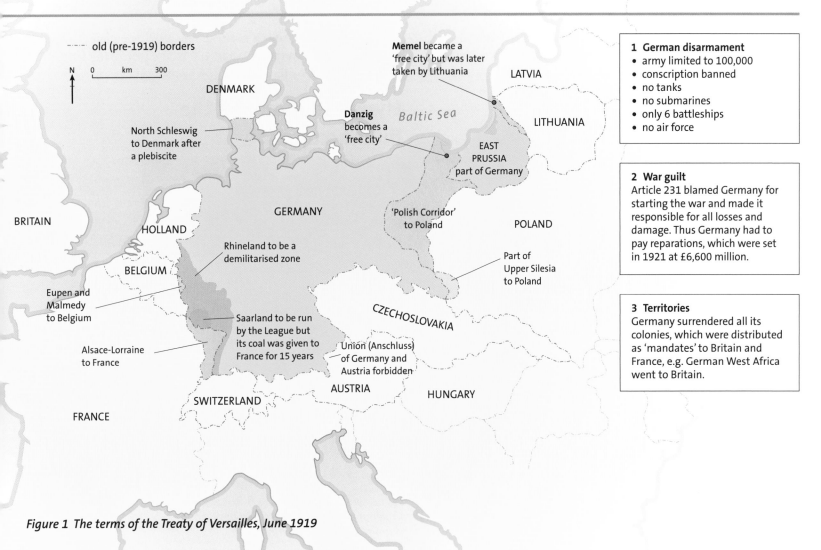

1 German disarmament
- army limited to 100,000
- conscription banned
- no tanks
- no submarines
- only 6 battleships
- no air force

2 War guilt
Article 231 blamed Germany for starting the war and made it responsible for all losses and damage. Thus Germany had to pay reparations, which were set in 1921 at £6,600 million.

3 Territories
Germany surrendered all its colonies, which were distributed as 'mandates' to Britain and France, e.g. German West Africa went to Britain.

Map labels:

— · — · old (pre-1919) borders

N
0   km   300

Memel became a 'free city' but was later taken by Lithuania

LATVIA

DENMARK

North Schleswig to Denmark after a plebiscite

Danzig becomes a 'free city'

Baltic Sea

LITHUANIA

EAST PRUSSIA part of Germany

GERMANY

'Polish Corridor' to Poland

POLAND

BRITAIN

HOLLAND

Rhineland to be a demilitarised zone

BELGIUM

Eupen and Malmedy to Belgium

Saarland to be run by the League but its coal was given to France for 15 years

Part of Upper Silesia to Poland

CZECHOSLOVAKIA

Alsace-Lorraine to France

Union (Anschluss) of Germany and Austria forbidden

SWITZERLAND

AUSTRIA

HUNGARY

FRANCE

Figure 1 The terms of the Treaty of Versailles, June 1919

However, the extreme left were never likely to seize political power because they were poorly coordinated and not well led. In addition, the revolts were brutally crushed by the army and the *Freikorps* under the orders of the Weimar government.

The extreme right

Many right-wing groups were drawn together from the beginning owing to their dislike of the Weimar Republic. Right-wing groups tended to attract support from army generals, landowners, the *Freikorps* and the civil service because they believed that:

- democracy was weak, which had contributed to Germany's problems (see the 'stab-in-the-back myth' on page 6)
- strong government and leadership with the Kaiser and the army could re-establish the 'old Germany'
- communism was a real threat to property and wealth

As a result, there were various anti-democratic parties, but the majority were small (e.g. the Nazi Party). The most significant party was the **Nationalists (DNVP)**. It won 10–15% of the vote in the Reichstag elections of 1919 and 1920. However, the extreme right also used more violent methods such as:

- The **Kapp Putsch** (March 1920). Discontent increased in the army ranks because the government planned to reduce their size. This led to a putsch (an uprising) of 5,000 soldiers. Led by **Wolfgang Kapp**, they marched on Berlin and took control of the capital. Other army leaders were generally sympathetic and they refused to crush the revolt against 'fellow troops'. However, the leaders of the Kapp Putsch could not maintain control as the trade unions declared a general strike and within a few days the revolt collapsed.

- Hitler's **Munich Putsch** in November 1923 (see page 25).
- **Terrorism**. Between 1919 and 1922 there were 376 political murders — 22 by the left and 354 by the right.

Hyperinflation and the Ruhr occupation

ILLUSTRATED LONDON NEWS

Children playing with devalued bank notes during Germany's hyperinflation

In 1914 Germany was the most powerful economy in Europe. However, after the First World War Germany faced growing inflation and had serious economic problems. In simple terms, this was because from 1914, Germany had borrowed too much money and had large debts because of the costs of the war, the welfare reforms and reparations. Moreover, this spending was only met by printing more money and this made the inflation increasingly worse.

The growing inflation problem got so out of hand in early 1923 that the German economy declined into **hyperinflation**. The printing of more and more money spiralled prices completely out of control. This started when Germany failed to pay its reparations instalment, which led to France and Belgium deciding in January 1923 to send their troops to occupy the Ruhr, Germany's key industrial region. The French and Belgians hoped to seize the coal and iron to make up for the reparations, but the Weimar government resorted to a policy of 'passive resistance'. The German workers did not cooperate with the occupying forces and went on strike.

By the summer of 1923 Germany's currency was in effect valueless and industrial production had collapsed. Some Germans did make real gains by paying off debts in useless money, but many were ruined because of the loss of their savings.

🔑 Key question

Was the Weimar Republic doomed from the start?

Table 3 Was the Weimar Republic doomed from the start?

Yes, the Weimar Republic was doomed because it had so many serious problems.	■ It was blamed by many for the Treaty of Versailles. ■ It faced fundamental economic problems. ■ It faced opposition from the extreme left and extreme right.
However, the Weimar Republic had managed to survive during the difficulties of 1918–23.	■ The uprisings had been crushed. ■ It had created a democratic republic with a constitution and still enjoyed the support of most German people. ■ When Stresemann was appointed as chancellor in 1923 he led the way to recovery from 1924 to 1929.

Use the information on pages 3–9, your class notes and your textbooks to answer the following questions.

1 Complete the chart by listing the following events in the correct chronological order and including the dates.

- French–Belgian occupation of the Ruhr
- Abdication of the emperor and the declaration of a German Republic
- Armistice
- Treaty of Versailles
- Kapp Putsch
- Weimar Constitution
- The naval mutiny
- Spartacist uprising

2 Explain how each of these factors led to the abdication of the Kaiser:
a the military defeat of Germany
b increasing social and economic problems
c the influence of the socialist movement

3 List two major differences between the Social Democrats and the Spartacists.

1

Date	Event
	The naval mutiny
11 November 1918	

2a ....

b ....
....
....

c ....
....
....

3 ....
....
....
....
....

Questions

4 Write brief notes in the diagram to explain the problems faced by Ebert's new government.

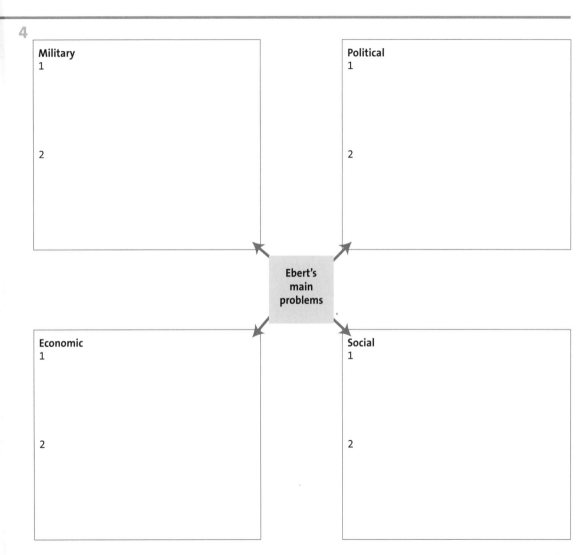

4

Military
1

2

Political
1

2

Ebert's main problems

Economic
1

2

Social
1

2

5 Complete *both* columns in the table with a tick or a cross to explain the differences between Germany in 1914 and in 1919.

5

	Germany in 1914	**Germany in 1919**
Democracy		
Soviet republic		
Autocracy		
Parliamentary republic		
Monarchy		

6 Complete the table to show the strengths and weaknesses of each aspect of the Weimar Constitution.

6

The Weimar Constitution	**Strengths**	**Weaknesses**
Proportional representation		
President		
Rights		

Questions

7 Explain the following terms carefully:
  a the 'Diktat'
  b the 'stab-in-the-back myth'
  c the 'November criminals'

7a

b

c

8 Explain why so many Germans felt the Treaty of Versailles was unfair.

8

9 Study Source A. Do you think this source was published by a supporter or opponent of the Weimar Republic? Use the source and your own knowledge to explain your answer.

Source A

'We refuse to buckle under to this military dictatorship. We did not bring about the revolution to make this bloody *Freikorps* regiment legal. Workers, Comrades...Go on strike, put down your work and stop the military dictatorship.'

A political appeal in March 1920

9

Source B
A German government poster produced in 1923. The German worker says to the French troops: *'No! You can't force me!'*

MARY EVANS/WEIMAR ARCHIVE

10

....

....

....

....

....

....

....

....

....

....

....

....

....

....

....

....

....

....

....

10 Study Source B and explain why the German people were angered by the events in 1923. Use the source and your own knowledge to explain your answer.

....

....

....

....

Questions

11 a Complete the table about the political strengths and weaknesses of the extremists.

	Strengths	Weaknesses
Extreme left		The uprisings were brutally crushed by a combination of the army and the *Freikorps*.
Extreme right		

b Which was the greater threat to the Weimar Republic in the years 1918–23 — the extreme left or the extreme right?

12 a Give three factors to explain why Germany suffered hyperinflation in 1923.

b Which factor was the most important? Explain your answer.

Source C
Cartoon published by a German magazine in 1923 with the title 'Paper money, Paper money'. The mother screams 'Bread! Bread!'

MARY EVANS PICTURE LIBRARY

13

13 Study Source C. How far does this cartoon explain why Germans faced difficulties in 1923? Use the source and your own knowledge to explain your answer.

Extended writing

On separate paper, write a short essay in answer to the following question.

14 Was inflation the most important reason for Germany's problems in the years 1919–23?

Key question

How far did the Weimar Republic recover by 1929?

Key content

- Political stability and the role of Stresemann
- Economic recovery
- Cultural achievements

Political stability under Stresemann

 What were Stresemann's achievements and limitations?

Stresemann's government, 1923

By the summer of 1923 the German economy had collapsed and there was no real government direction. However, as chancellor from August 1923 Gustav Stresemann took several important decisions to deal with the crisis:

- Passive resistance was ended and Germany promised to resume reparations.
- Government spending was cut to reduce the deficit.
- A new currency, the Rentenmark, was introduced to replace the old notes.
- In discussion with the Allies, the Dawes Committee was created to examine Germany's financial situation (which became the Dawes Plan in 1924, see page 18).

Stresemann also maintained political control despite a number of disturbances. The strikes by the left were defeated by the army and the attempted putsch by Hitler and the Nazis crushed by the Bavarian police (see page 25).

Gustav Stresemann, 1878–1929

Although Gustav Stresemann remained a monarchist, he is generally seen as the most influential politician in republican Weimar Germany in the 1920s. He was only chancellor for 3 months in 1923, but he served in every government in the years 1923–29 and directed foreign affairs. At the age of just 51 he died in the same month as the beginning of the great American economic crash.

Political strengths

- The election results gave grounds for hope for the survival of the Weimar Republic (see Table 1 on page 18). In 1928 support for the extremists declined and the pro-democracy parties recovered strength.
- There were no more major uprisings against the Weimar Republic after the troubles of 1918–23.
- Field Marshal von Hindenburg was elected president in 1925. Because of his stature, he acted as a figurehead for the country.

Political weaknesses

- The political parties found it difficult to cooperate. There were seven different governments in the years 1924–30. The longest survived just 21 months.

- Hindenburg was a nationalist and was not sympathetic to Weimar democracy. He was an old man and close to the army generals and landowners whose support for the republic was limited.

Table 1 Elections 1924–28

	May 1924	May 1928
No. of Reichstag seats	472	491
Nazis	32	12
Nationalists	95	73
Social Democrats	100	153
Other pro-democrats	154	148
Communists	62	54
Other seats	29	51

Foreign affairs

Most Germans were determined to bring about an end to the terms of the Treaty of Versailles. Some political leaders believed that the treaty's terms should be resisted wherever possible. Others simply believed that Germany's weak position made it impossible to pursue an ambitious foreign policy.

From 1923–29 German foreign affairs were under the control of Stresemann. He was a strong patriot but he was also a realist. He believed that Germany should concentrate on reconciliation:

- The **Dawes Plan** (1924) did not reduce the reparations sum, but the monthly instalments were changed according to Germany's ability to pay. It also provided for a large loan from the USA to aid German economic recovery.
- By the **Locarno Pact** (1925) France, Germany and Belgium agreed to accept the western borders, and the demilitarisation of the Rhineland was recognised as permanent.
- By the **Treaty of Versailles** Germany was excluded from the League of Nations, but in 1926 Germany was invited to join.
- The Allies agreed to evacuate all their military personnel from the **Rhineland**, which had been occupied since the war.
- The **Young Plan** (1929) revised the scheme of reparations payments and the total sum was reduced to one-quarter of the original figure.

Stresemann's success

Stresemann achieved a great deal in a short time, especially bearing in mind the desperate state Germany had been in during the period 1918–23. However, he failed to achieve his aim to revise Versailles fundamentally. In particular, his ambition to change the German–Polish frontiers came to nothing. As a result, Stresemann did not enjoy much popular support in Weimar Germany — and the Nationalists and Nazis from the right wing loathed him.

The Weimar economy

 What were the strengths and weaknesses of the Weimar economic recovery?

Strengths
- Stresemann's decisions in the latter half of 1923 helped to restore economic confidence, e.g. the creation of the Rentenmark, the Dawes Plan (see page 18).
- Big business, especially coal and steel, recovered well and by 1928 production levels had reached those of 1913.
- German exports rose by 40% between 1925 and 1929.
- Wages rose for industrial workers every year from 1924 to 1930.
- The Weimar governments increased public spending on housing and schools.

Weaknesses
- Even before the world depression began to be felt (1929), unemployment never fell below 1.3 million in the 1920s.
- Many farmers were in debt and faced falling incomes/wages after the war.
- Small businessmen felt squeezed out by the power of big business and the large department stores.
- Investment into Germany increased substantially, but the economy became too reliant on investment from abroad, especially the USA.
- Germany continued to face serious finance problems. From 1925 the Weimar governments remained in debt. And despite the recovery, Germany continued to import more than it exported.

As a result, the performance of the Weimar economy was mixed. It did not provide the basis for solid economic growth and its future was precarious.

Cultural achievements

? In what ways was Weimar seen as a culturally rich period?

There was an explosion of culture in the 1920s. Artists and writers enjoyed great freedom during the Weimar years and they were able to experiment with new ideas. The most well-known figures in their fields of that time were:
- Otto Dix (artist)
- Walter Gropius (designer and the founder of the Bauhaus movement)
- Erich Maria von Remarque (author, who wrote the anti-war book *All Quiet on the Western Front*)
- Bertolt Brecht (playwright)

This free-thinking atmosphere coincided with the development of a mass culture:
- Cinemas opened in most German towns — and films were popular even before the production of the 'talkies' in 1928.
- The German Radio Company was established in 1923 and, by 1932, one in four Germans owned a radio.

- In the capital, Berlin, the nightclubs and parties contributed to the 'Cabaret' image of a good-living lifestyle.

Of course, Berlin was not typical of all German towns. In fact, many Germans saw the capital as corrupt, and contributing to a decline of moral standards and German values.

🔑 Key question

How far did the Weimar Republic recover by 1929?

The years 1924–29 are often seen as a 'Golden Age' in contrast to the troubles of 1918–23 and the Great Depression of 1929–33 that led to mass unemployment, Hitler's rise to power and the end of democracy (see Topic 3). However, Weimar Germany's recovery was not all it seemed. It had a range of strengths and achievements:

- It achieved economic stability after the crisis of economic hyperinflation, but it still had fundamental weaknesses, which were disguised, e.g. the over-dependence on American loans.
- It experienced a political calm after the uprisings and violence of the political extremists and this encouraged the chances of Weimar democracy's success. However, it still faced powerful right-wing opponents who did not support Weimar, e.g. the army generals and the judges.
- It had overcome its isolation and returned to the international stage, yet many Germans still blamed Weimar for the Armistice and Treaty of Versailles.
- It was a period of great cultural creativity, but not all Germans liked it — especially the conservatives who wanted to restore traditional values.

So, despite the recovery Weimar Germany was a weak and divided society.

Questions

Use the information on pages 17–20, your class notes and your textbooks to answer the following questions.

1 Define and explain what is meant by the following terms:

a Rentenmark
b Dawes Plan
c 'talkies'
d 'Golden Age'

1a

b

c

d

2 Complete *both* columns in the table with a tick or a cross to indicate the political views of Stresemann and Hindenburg.

2

	Gustav Stresemann: Chancellor, 1923; Foreign Minister, 1923–29	Marshal Hindenburg: President, 1925–34
Democrat		
Monarchist		
Parliamentarian		
Socialist		
Nationalist		
Conservative		

3 There were seven different governments in the Weimar years 1924–30. Give two reasons to explain why it was so difficult for the political parties to achieve clear and stable leadership of the Weimar Republic.

3

Source A

Year	Unemploy- ment (%)	Industrial production. (1928 base = 100)
1913	3.0	98
1921	1.8	65
1923	4.1	46
1925	3.4	81
1926	10.0	78
1927	6.2	98
1928	6.3	100
1929	8.5	100

Source B

...a new government under Stresemann took over. He called off the passive resistance. After the crisis of the hyperinflation, the German economy began to revive. The new currency brought stability and removed the fear of inflation.

British historian, 2005

4 What can you learn from Source A about the recovery of the German economy?

5 Use Source B and your own knowledge to explain how Stresemann's economic policy helped Germany to overcome the economic crisis of 1923.

6 Explain what you can learn from Table 1 on page 18 about the political parties in the election results.

4

5

6

Questions

Source C

He [Stresemann] saw you can only serve your people by understanding other peoples. To serve collapsed Germany he set on the path of understanding. Being a practical man he [Stresemann] saw that any other path would have left Germany without any hope of recovery...

Obituary from *Vorwärts*, the SPD newspaper, in October 1929

Source D

Cheers to the New Year!

Five years of Stresemann. Free yourself of the red chains! Be quiet. Say no more. The red chains have stayed...It is true the spirit of Dawes and Locarno has descended upon us and has not eased the great deprivation of our people. But Stresemann remains with us...Five years of Stresemann: the German foreign policy is a scene of devastation. We have given and the others have taken with scorn and without gratitude.

Article by J. Goebbels in *Der Angriff* of 31 December 1928

7 a Read Sources C and D. Do they agree on Stresemann's political reputation?

b Explain possible reasons why these two interpretations are different.

8 Complete the table to show how significant each aspect of Weimar culture was in the 1920s.

Extended writing

On separate paper, write a short essay in answer to the following question.

9 How far had the Weimar Republic recovered from its problems by spring 1929?

7a

b

8

Aspect	Significance
Radio	
Cinema	
Berlin 'Cabaret' image	
The Bauhaus movement	
E. M. Remarque	

Why did the Weimar Republic collapse and why was Hitler able to become chancellor?

Key content

- Hitler's early career and the foundation of the Nazi Party: main Nazi ideas and political methods
- The failure of the 1923 Munich Putsch and the rebuilding of the party
- Impact of the Depression
- Rise of the Nazi Party, 1930–33: elections 1930 and 1932; other key Nazi leaders; propaganda
- Appointment of Hitler as chancellor

Hitler and the establishment of the Nazi Party

 How did the Nazi Party develop its early ideas and organisation?

Postwar Germany had many extreme right-wing political organisations. However, it was not until the Great Depression in the early 1930s that Adolf Hitler and the Nazi Party made any real political impact. The early development of the party and the role of Hitler can be seen in Table 1.

Table 1 Early development of the Nazi Party and Hitler's role

1919	German Workers' Party (DAP) was created by **Anton Drexler**.
	Hitler joined the party as a member of the *Freikorps*.
1920	The 25-point programme was drawn up by Drexler and Hitler. The party was renamed the **NSDAP** (National Socialist German Workers' Party) — also known as the Nazis.
1921	Hitler became the leader of the party and arranged: — the setting up of the **SA**, a private army led by **Ernst Röhm** (the Brownshirts or Stormtroopers) — the creation of its own newspaper, the *Völkischer Beobachter* (the People's Observer).
1923	The failure of the **Beer Hall Putsch** at Munich.
1924	Hitler found guilty of treason and sentenced to 5 years in prison. Served 10 months at Landsberg prison and wrote *Mein Kampf* ('My Struggle').

The main ideas of Nazism

Nazism was based on the 25-point programme of the DAP and Hitler's book *Mein Kampf*:

- **Nationalism**. To unite all German-speaking people and to abolish the Treaty of Versailles.
- **Racism**. To develop a racially pure German state. For Hitler, the 'master race' were the Aryans (the people of northern Europe), and the Germans represented the highest. For Hitler the lowest race were the Jews.

- **Social Darwinism**. Hitler viewed the world as a struggle between peoples, races and nations. He was deeply influenced by the theory of evolution based on natural selection and viewed life as the 'survival of the fittest'.
- **Anti-democracy**. Hitler believed that democracy was weak and the Weimar Republic could not provide the strong leadership needed for Germany. Hitler therefore called for a **Führer** ('leader') and the establishment of a **one-party state**.
- **Anti-communism**. To oppose the rise and spread of communism.
- **Expansionism**. To create an empire and to make Germany into a great power. Hitler expected to establish German supremacy over the eastern lands in Europe, e.g. Poland and Russia, and to exploit the labour and resources there. Hitler referred to this as **Lebensraum** or 'living space'.

The Beer Hall Munich Putsch, 1923

In the early 1920s the Nazi Party earned quite a reputation around Bavaria. Both Hitler's own powerful speeches and SA violence gained support from the pub crowds and influential members of Bavarian society. However, the growth of the party was limited.

The Weimar crisis in 1923 (see Topic 1) encouraged Hitler to organise a putsch. He gained the support of some leading political conservatives in Bavaria who opposed the democratic republic and together they planned to 'March on Berlin'. However, when it came to the day of the putsch some of the leading players lost their nerve and the Nazis had insufficient military support — the

attempted takeover of Munich on 9 November 1923 was therefore easily crushed by the Bavarian police.

The putsch was a fiasco. Fourteen Nazis were killed and some of the leaders were arrested on a charge of treason; the party was also banned. Yet, Hitler benefited from the episode:
- Hitler's trial made him a national figure for the first time.
- He made some impressive speeches and turned the trial into a propaganda success both for himself and for the Nazi cause.
- In prison he wrote *Mein Kampf* and thought through his political strategy.

The rebuilding of the Nazi Party

 Why did the Nazis have only limited success before 1930?

Hitler was released from prison after serving just 10 months, although his sentence for treason had been 5 years. Yet, the outlook for the Nazi Party was not optimistic. It had become bitterly divided and the Weimar Republic was showing signs of recovery (see Topic 2).

Nevertheless, in the years 1924–29 the Nazi Party laid the basis for its future success:
- **The legality policy**. After the failure of the putsch, Hitler persuaded the party to seek power legally. Therefore, in order to undermine Weimar democracy and win power, the party aimed to gain as many Nazi seats in the Reichstag as possible.
- **Leadership**. Hitler re-established his authority. He overcame the party's internal bickering and policy differences. It was

decided to run the party according to the **Führerprinzip** (leadership principle), which did not allow for any disagreements.

- **Party organisation**. The party was restructured and organised into 35 regions, each one with a local leader called a *Gauleiter*. This laid the basis for a structure to win mass electoral support — and by 1929 the party had a good membership base.

Many of the party's later key organisations were established in the 1920s:

- the Hitler Youth
- the SS (later to be led by Heinrich Himmler)
- **Joseph Goebbels** emerged as a vital and loyal figure who cleverly used propaganda to advance the cause of the Nazi Party (see page 28).

In one sense the Nazi Party had made good progress. Its membership had increased significantly — from 27,000 in 1925 to 108,000 in 1928. On the other hand, in the 1928 Reichstag election it attracted only 2.8% of the national vote and won a mere 12 seats. Hitler himself was viewed generally as an eccentric character. It seemed as if the party had come to a dead end.

The impact of the Depression

 Why did Weimar fail to cope with the economic and political crisis?

In October 1929 the Weimar Republic was hit by two blows:

- Stresemann died at the age of 51.
- The New York stock exchange on Wall Street crashed and financial investments fell.

The Great Depression, 1929–33

In 1929 the stock exchange on Wall Street in New York collapsed. This led to an economic depression across the world (though not the USSR). Trade declined and by 1932 there were 12 million unemployed in the USA, 6 million in Germany and 3 million in Britain. The economic depression lasted well into the 1930s and millions suffered great hardship.

Germany was hit particularly badly because of its dependence on American loans. From 1929–33 it suffered major economic problems:

- Trade collapsed.
- Mass unemployment climbed to 6.1 million registered in 1932.
- Industrial production declined by 40%.
- Prices fell (deflation, *not* inflation). The income of farmers fell, leading to debts.
- Major banks collapsed.

Weimar's political crisis

As a result, by 1930 Weimar Germany faced not only an economic, but also a political, crisis. The government was split on how to deal with the Depression and in March 1930 it resigned. Heinrich Brüning, the leader of the Centre Party, was appointed chancellor, but he did not have a majority in the Reichstag and this led to the problems getting worse:

- The Reichstag was dissolved and pro-democratic parties lost support after the election of September 1930, whereas the Nazis made a real breakthrough (see Table 2 on page 27).

- Brüning remained as chancellor from 1930 to 1932, but he could only govern Germany by the use of decrees from President Hindenburg (see Article 48 on page 5). In effect, parliamentary democracy had given way to a semi-dictatorship.
- Brüning's policy was to cut spending and raise taxes in order to reduce government debt. This proved unpopular and he was mocked by the title of the 'Hunger Chancellor'.

Brüning survived because he kept the support of Hindenburg, but by 1932 when the Depression was at its worst point the aged president forced him to resign.

The rise of the Nazis, 1930–33

 How and why did the Nazis gain so much support?

The 1928 Reichstag election had been disappointing for the Nazis. However, as the effects of the Depression worsened, they made an electoral breakthrough:
- In the **September 1930 Reichstag election** the Nazis gained 107 seats (18%) and became the second largest party in the country.
- In the **presidential election of April 1932** Hitler lost to President Hindenburg, but he still gained 37% of the vote.
- In the **July 1932 Reichstag election** the Nazis gained 230 seats (37%) and became by far the largest party.

The details of the Reichstag election results can be seen in Table 2. The main trends show clearly that:
- In 2 years the Nazis had changed from being a fringe party into the most powerful one in the country.

- The Communists had also significantly increased their vote.
- All the pro-democratic parties had declined.

The difficult times played a vital role in explaining the rise of Nazism, though it seems some groups were more attracted to the Nazis than others. For example:
- the Protestants (rather than the Catholics)
- the young aged 18–30
- the lower middle class, e.g. shopkeepers
- the peasants
- the established middle class, e.g. teachers

Table 2 Election results, 1928–32

Election results, 1928–32		May 1928	September 1930	July 1932
No. of Reichstag seats		491	577	608
Nazis	seats	12	107	230
	% of vote	2.6	18.3	37.3
Nationalists	seats	73	41	37
	% of vote	14.2	7.0	5.9
Social Democrats	seats	153	143	133
	% of vote	29.8	24.5	21.6
Other pro-democratic parties	seats	148	137	101
	% of vote	28.8	22.3	17.9
Communists	seats	54	77	89
	% of vote	10.8	13.1	14.3
Other parties	seats	51	72	11
	% of vote	14.0	13.8	2.9

Nazi propaganda

Hitler and Goebbels cleverly played on the weakness of Weimar democracy and German fears of communism to win support. They also exploited the scapegoat of the Jews. In addition, because of the social and economic circumstances they appealed to the peasants by offering particular benefits against the collapse of agricultural prices and to the industrial workers with 'bread' and 'work'. Finally, Nazism tried to unify as many Germans as possible:

- by portraying Hitler as a strong authoritarian leader
- by appealing to German nationalism to make the country great again after the Treaty of Versailles

However, it was not only the Nazi message that won support. What really made Nazism stand out was the technology and style of the Nazi propaganda organised by Goebbels. He adapted the new technology of loudspeakers, radio broadcasts and film in order to convey a mass appeal. And he even carefully arranged large parades and rallies of thousands of people that created a uniting atmosphere known as 'mass suggestion'.

Nazi violence

The Nazis deliberately used violence in their rise to power. Weimar politics had always been a bloody affair, but the growth of unemployment resulted in a phenomenal expansion of the SA led by Röhm (see Topic 4, page 39). Understandably, many joined as members of the SA out of desperation for food and accommodation. However, the SA was mainly responsible for the intimidation and violence against the opposition, especially the socialists

Doctor Joseph Goebbels (1897–1945)

Although Goebbels joined the NSDAP in 1922, he only committed himself to Hitler in 1926. Soon afterwards he was appointed Nazi leader of Berlin (*Gauleiter*).

Goebbels was one of the few Nazi intellectuals and he was a first-class speaker. In 1928 he was put in charge of party

ILLUSTRATED LONDON NEWS

propaganda. From then he played a key role in cultivating the leadership of Hitler and the rise of the Nazis in the elections of 1930–32.

Soon after Hitler's appointment as chancellor, Goebbels was appointed as Minister of Propaganda in March 1933, a position he retained until his suicide in 1945. He therefore played a crucial role in strengthening the Nazi regime by using all the skills of propaganda and censorship (see also Topic 5, pages 47–48).

and communists — on one day in the presidential election of 1932 ten people were killed in political riots.

Conspiracy, 1932–33

? How and why was Hitler appointed chancellor in January 1933?

The 9 months leading up to Hitler's appointment as chancellor on 30 January 1933 were full of intrigue. It was a complex period of history (see Table 3).

Germany was descending into economic and political chaos. The Nazis had gained a large proportion of popular support. However, President Hindenburg did not really like Hitler and had no desire to appoint him as chancellor. Many of the conservatives in Germany, including the army, landowners and industrialists, were suspicious of Hitler and his party. So why did the conservatives fail to control the situation and why did Hindenburg eventually appoint Hitler?

Table 3 Key events and dates, 1932–33

1932	April	Presidential election: Hindenburg re-elected, but Hitler gained 37% of the vote.
	May	Brüning dismissed as chancellor and replaced by Papen.
	July	Reichstag election. Nazis = 230 seats (37%).
	November	Reichstag vote down Papen's government (512–42).
		Reichstag election. Nazis = 196 seats.
	December	Papen dismissed as chancellor and replaced by Schleicher.
1933	27 January	Schleicher dismissed as chancellor.
	30 January	Hitler appointed as chancellor with Papen as vice-chancellor.

Hindenburg dismissed Brüning as chancellor in May 1932 and appointed first Franz von Papen and then Kurt von Schleicher. However, neither was able to provide stable government. They did not have enough support from the Reichstag and they both depended on the use of presidential decrees. In contrast, the Nazis had clearly become the largest party and so Hitler demanded the post of chancellor for himself.

Hitler's eventual appointment grew out of the personal rivalry between Papen and Schleicher. In early January 1933 Papen started to organise a series of secret meetings with a range of some of Germany's conservatives. They aimed to persuade Hindenburg to dismiss Schleicher and to replace him with Hitler as the head of a Nationalist–Nazi coalition government.

Therefore, despite the doubts of many, Hindenburg agreed to appoint Hitler as chancellor on 30 January 1933, with Papen as vice-chancellor, in the belief that Hitler could be controlled.

🔑 Key question

Why did the Weimar Republic collapse and why was Hitler able to become chancellor?

The Weimar Republic had fundamental weaknesses from the start:
- It had struggled to survive in the years 1919–23, e.g. the blow of the Treaty of Versailles and the effects of the hyperinflation.
- Even in its 'golden years' Weimar merely coped and faced serious problems. It was largely dependent on US loans.

- The Weimar crisis was undoubtedly prompted by the Depression, but by 1930 the governments of Brüning, Papen and Schleicher were not really democratic.

Hitler and the Nazis were able to exploit the situation successfully for four key reasons:
- Hitler's character and style of leadership led to him being viewed as a saviour.
- The Nazi Party's organisation and propaganda were superior.
- SA violence made it difficult to control the situation.
- Nazism developed a mass support of 37% by 1932 — and was clearly the largest party.

Yet, it would be wrong to assume that the appointment of Hitler and the creation of a Nazi dictatorship were inevitable. The Weimar governments of 1932 were not able to give stability and leadership — and it is for this reason that Papen and other German conservatives persuaded Hindenburg to appoint Hitler as chancellor in the hope that he could be tamed.

Questions

Use the information on pages 24–30, your class notes and textbooks to answer the following questions.

1 Define and explain what is meant by the following terms:
  a NSDAP
  b SA
  c *Mein Kampf*
  d *Gauleiter*
  e Mass suggestion

1a ....

b ....

c ....

d ....

e ....

2 Complete the chart by listing the following events in the correct chronological order:
  ■ Munich Beer Hall Putsch
  ■ Drexler formed the DAP
  ■ Hitler appointed as chancellor
  ■ 25-point programme of NSDAP drawn up
  ■ SA formed
  ■ Hitler became leader of the party
  ■ Wall Street Crash
  ■ Nazis became the largest party in the Reichstag
  ■ Hitler tried and imprisoned
  ■ Goebbels placed in charge of the party's propaganda

Date	Event
1919	
	Hitler became leader of the party
1933	

Source A

The meeting, which was well attended, came to an early end because of an attack by the National Socialists. Nazi youths had taken seats near the speakers' platform and many of them were distributed through the hall. When Hitler, their leader, appeared in the hall, he was greeted with loud applause from his followers. His arrival was a sign for the violence that followed. Someone climbed on a chair and shouted that the current situation was all the fault of the Jews. The lights went out briefly, and then the Nazis rushed the platform, grabbed the speaker and beat him up. The police came and ended the meeting.

Report in a Munich newspaper, September 1921

3 What does Source A tell us about the political methods of Hitler and the Nazis?

4 Complete the table to explain the main ideas of Hitler and the Nazi Party.

3

....
....
....
....
....
....
....
....

4

Key ideas	Explanation
Nationalism	
Racism	
Social Darwinism	
Anti-democracy	
Anti-communism	
Expansionism	

Questions

5 To what extent was the Munich Putsch a disaster for the Nazi Party? Look at both the achievements and the failures of the Nazis.

5

6 Read Source B, which was written by Hitler while in prison in 1924.

6a

> **Source B**
> When I resume active work it will be necessary to pursue a new policy. Instead of working to achieve power by arms, we shall have to hold our noses and enter the Reichstag against the Catholic and Socialist deputies.

b

a What do you think Hitler meant by this statement?

b Describe the key developments which occurred in the rebuilding of the Nazi party after 1924.

c

c How successful was the Nazi Party with Hitler's 'new policy' by 1928?

7 Why was Weimar Germany so susceptible to the stock market crash on Wall Street in October 1929?

7

8 a Describe and explain two economic consequences of the Great Depression in Germany.

8a

b Describe and explain two political consequences of the Great Depression for Weimar Germany.

b

9 Examine the Reichstag election results on Table 2 on page 27. What does the source tell you about the changing fortunes of the parties?

9

Questions

10 Read Source C. What can you learn from Source C about who supported the Nazis in the elections of 1930–32?

10

11 a What were the key features of the Nazi message in Nazi propaganda?

11a

b In what ways did Goebbels use propaganda effectively to spread the Nazi message?

b

12 Examine Source D. Explain why this poster was published in 1932. In your answer, make sure that you examine the purpose of the Nazis in publishing the poster at that time. What was going on in Germany in 1932? Use your own knowledge to help develop your answer.

Source D

Election poster: the title translates as 'Our last hope'.

IMPERIAL WAR MUSEUM MH13569

Extended writing

On separate paper, write a short essay in answer to the following question.

13 'Hitler was able to become chancellor in January 1933 only because of the effects of the Depression.' Do you agree?

12

🔑 Key question

How and why was the Nazi dictatorship created so quickly?

🔑 Key content

The Nazis' consolidation of power:
- the Reichstag Fire
- the Enabling Law
- coordination

The Night of the Long Knives:
- the role of the army and the SS
- the death of Hindenburg

The Nazis' consolidation of power

 How did Hitler manage to establish his power so quickly?

When Hitler was appointed chancellor in January 1933, Papen claimed that he would be a 'chancellor in chains'. It is certainly true that Hitler was not a dictator at first. In fact, his position was quite insecure for several reasons:
- Hitler was only chancellor of a coalition government. In Hitler's twelve-man cabinet there were only two Nazis.
- President Hindenburg still had the power to dismiss Hitler as chancellor and he did not personally like him.
- The coalition government did not have a majority in the Reichstag and so it would be difficult to pass any new laws to increase Hitler's powers.

Yet, within just a few months the Nazi dictatorship was to be firmly established.

The 'Reichstag Fire'

Immediately after becoming chancellor, Hitler called for another Reichstag election. He hoped to win more seats and gain a convincing majority for the Nazi Party in order to change the Weimar Constitution.

However, on 27 February 1933 the Reichstag in Berlin was engulfed in fire. Soon after a young communist, Van der Lubbe, was arrested. The exact cause of the fire still remains unclear and controversial, but undoubtedly the Nazis used the event to strengthen their position. Hitler persuaded Hindenburg to sign an emergency decree which suspended many of the country's civil and political rights. The communists were then conveniently blamed for the fire and many of their leaders were arrested.

The Enabling Law

The election of March 1933 allowed the Nazi Party to increase their vote to 44% and win 288 seats. However, any laws changing the constitution actually required a two-thirds majority of the Reichstag and the Nazis did not have an overall majority in the Reichstag.

Despite these political barriers, Hitler and the Nazi leaders decided to propose an Enabling Bill. This would grant the chancellor the power to issue decrees for 4 years without having to pass them through the Reichstag. When it came to the debate on 23 March 1933 the galleries of the temporary Reichstag were crowded by the SA who intimidated the Reichstag deputies with threats of violence. And because many Communist deputies were in prison following the Reichstag Fire and some of the other parties abstained due to intimidation, Hitler won the vote. Only the Social Democrats voted against the Enabling Bill. As a result, the Enabling Law allowed Hitler to rule by decree without reference to the Reichstag — he had become a kind of 'legal dictator'.

Coordination

Over the following months Hitler used these new powers to 'Nazify' Germany. This process has been called **coordination**. Coordination aimed to remove political opposition and to bring into line as many aspects of German life as possible.

Examples of Nazi coordination include:
- **Trade unions**. On 2 May leading trade unionists were arrested. During the same month all the free trade unions were abolished. From that time only the Nazi-organised German Labour Front existed to oversee the workers' interests (see Topic 6, page 65).
- **Political parties**. During the summer of 1933 all political parties other than the NSDAP were closed down. In July 1933 'The Law against the Establishment of Parties' was declared. This made the NSDAP the only legal party in Germany.

- **Local and regional government**. Political power was centralised in Berlin. For example, all regional parliaments (e.g. Bavaria) were abolished in January 1934.

So by early 1934 Hitler had removed most opposition to him from outside the Nazi party. However, it was not possible for the Nazis to 'coordinate' some of the powerful forces in Germany straightaway, such as the army and the civil service.

The Night of the Long Knives

 Why did Hitler destroy the SA and why was the purge so significant?

A fundamental problem remained at the heart of political power in Germany. The SA, led by **Ernst Röhm**, had played a major part in the violence of the rise of the Nazis (see Topic 3, page 28). It had also willingly helped with the process of coordination. In addition, Röhm himself had the personal aim of creating a 'people's army' merged from the army and the SA. Such talk seriously alarmed the conservative forces in Germany, especially the German army's generals, and they became keen to tame the SA in order to preserve their own interests.

This presented Hitler with a political and personal dilemma. In the end he decided to act and he threw in his lot with the army against the SA. As a result, on 30 June 1934 he ruthlessly ordered SS squads to purge the SA. In what became known as the **Night of the Long Knives**, 400 SA leaders, including Röhm, were killed. Hitler also took the opportunity to settle various old scores by executing victims, such as ex-chancellor Schleicher.

Ernst Röhm (1887–1934)

Röhm was an ex-soldier and an early member of the party who helped Hitler to form the SA in 1921. He then acted as the SA leader in the years 1921–23 until the collapse of the Beer Hall Putsch.

Röhm was reappointed as SA leader, 1930–34, and played a crucial role in the intimidation and street violence of those years. However, from 1933 he wanted to merge the army and the SA into a 'people's army' and increasingly fell out with Hitler. His death along with 400 other leading SA men in the Night of the Long Knives decisively secured Hitler's personal political leadership.

The Night of the Long Knives was a turning point. With the purge of the SA, Hitler destroyed an increasingly powerful threat to his own position within the Nazi Party. What is more, in doing so, he gained the support of the German army — though the actual crimes were carried out by the increasingly influential SS.

As a result, when President Hindenburg died on 2 August 1934, Hitler was immediately able to strengthen his own authority by:

- combining both the offices of president and chancellor
- declaring himself Führer
- making the German army sign a personal oath of loyalty to himself

🔑 Key question

How and why was the Nazi dictatorship created so quickly?

- The Nazi leadership used the law effectively to back up the development of the dictatorship, e.g. the Enabling Law.
- The Nazis used terror to weaken opposition, e.g. the Communists and Social Democrats.
- Hitler cleverly portrayed himself in all the propaganda as a reasonable statesman.
- Although the Nazis never won a democratic majority, it should be remembered that from 1932 they were the largest party in Germany and they did have mass support.
- The conservative forces in Germany never strongly supported the Weimar Republic and once it began to decline they became more sympathetic to the Nazis.

Questions

Use the information on pages 37–39, your class notes and your textbooks to answer the following questions.

1 Complete the chart by listing the following events in the correct chronological order:
- Banning of free trade unions
- Reichstag Fire
- Hitler's appointment as chancellor
- Political parties banned except for the NSDAP
- Death of President Hindenburg and the German army swear an oath of allegiance to Hitler
- Abolition of all regional parliaments
- Last Reichstag election of the Weimar Constitution
- Night of the Long Knives
- Passing of the Enabling Law

2 Complete the table to explain how and why each factor was expected to limit Hitler's power when he was appointed as chancellor in January 1933.

1

Date	Event
30 January 1933	
	Passing of the Enabling Law

2

Factor	Explanation: how did each factor constrain Hitler's power?
Hitler was appointed as chancellor of a coalition government	
Hindenburg was still president	
Hitler and the Nazis did not have a majority in the Reichstag	

Questions

3 In what ways did the Reichstag Fire weaken the political opposition to the Nazis?

4 Explain what you can learn from Source A about the establishment of the Nazi dictatorship.

Source A

I showed my report to Göring. 'That's sheer rubbish,' he said. 'One sack of fire-lighting material! No, we must say one hundred sacks.' 'But that is impossible, Minister. No one can believe that a single man can have carried all that.' 'Nothing is impossible. We must say there were ten or even twenty men. The whole thing was a signal for a Communist uprising. They must have come through the tunnel.'

Göring's press officer describing his conversation with Göring shortly after the Reichstag Fire on 27 February 1933

5 a How did Hitler succeed in getting the Enabling Bill passed?

b Explain exactly how the Enabling Law strengthened Hitler's position as chancellor.

3

4

5a

b

6 a Define coordination.
  b Describe three main ways in which German life was coordinated in 1933–34.
  c Give two examples of German life which were not coordinated in 1933–34.

6a

b

c

7 a What were the main aims of Röhm and the SA?
  b What were the political aims of the German army's generals?
  c Explain how the Night of the Long Knives strengthened Hitler's position in 1934.

7a

b

c

Questions

8 Complete the chart to explain how Hitler overcame the weakness of his political position as chancellor in 1933 to become a dictator of Germany by the end of 1934.

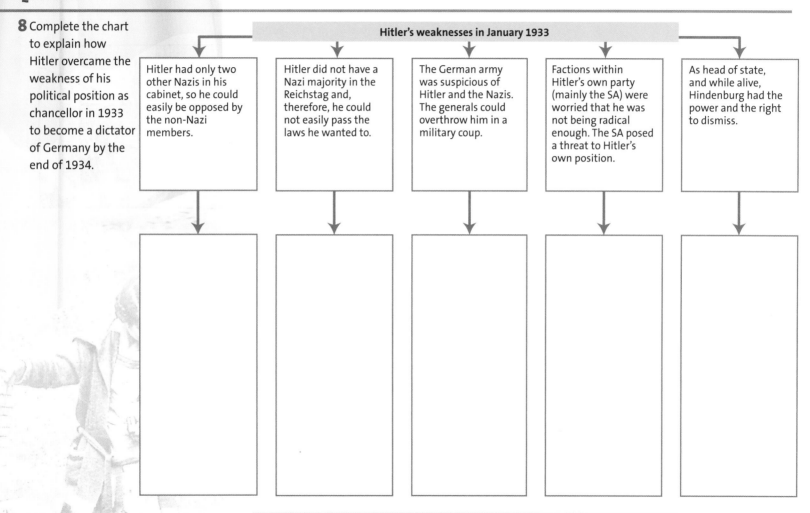

Hitler's weaknesses in January 1933

Hitler had only two other Nazis in his cabinet, so he could easily be opposed by the non-Nazi members.	Hitler did not have a Nazi majority in the Reichstag and, therefore, he could not easily pass the laws he wanted to.	The German army was suspicious of Hitler and the Nazis. The generals could overthrow him in a military coup.	Factions within Hitler's own party (mainly the SA) were worried that he was not being radical enough. The SA posed a threat to Hitler's own position.	As head of state, and while alive, Hindenburg had the power and the right to dismiss.

Weaknesses overcome by end 1934

9 How useful is Source B to a historian as evidence of what happened in Germany in the summer of 1934? Make sure that you consider both the usefulness and limitations of this cartoon.

9

Source B

DAVID LOW, EVENING STANDARD 3 JULY 1934/ BRITISH CARTOON ARCHIVE, UNIVERSITY OF KENT

British cartoon, July 1934. Its caption was: 'They saluted with both hands'.

Extended writing for Topics 3 and 4

On a separate piece of paper, write a short essay in answer to the following question.

10 'The most important factor that helped Hitler to strengthen his control over Germany during 1933 and 1934 was the Reichstag Fire.'

Remember to explain how the Reichstag Fire helped Hitler strengthen his position together with at least two other events.

Key question

How effectively did the Nazis control Germany in the years 1933–39?

Key content

- The Nazi state — methods of control and repression
- Propaganda and censorship — Nazi culture
- Persecution of minorities, including anti-Semitism

Nazi rule

 How was Germany ruled during the Third Reich?

The Nazis' aim was to turn Germany into a **totalitarian** state: the Nazis would have total control over all aspects of life and individual rights and freedoms would not exist. Hitler himself was portrayed as the all-mighty Führer at the head of a highly organised working Nazi state. However, the reality was rather more complex.

Hitler

From the summer of 1934 Hitler's personal power was in theory total (see Topic 4). He combined the posts of chancellor and president (and head of state). He took the title of **Der Führer** — the leader of the party and the German nation. He was also the military supreme commander. From that time, the number of meetings for the cabinet and Reichstag declined markedly.

Yet, Hitler had the following weaknesses:

- poor training and education
- poor work routine
- lazy and laid-back lifestyle
- moody and neurotic tendencies

In addition, many historians have drawn attention to Hitler's leadership limitations. It has even been suggested that he was a 'weak dictator' because:

- He did not organise and govern effectively.
- He could not control the other political forces in Germany.

The SS

The **SS (Schutz Staffel)** was originally a small group of Hitler's elite personal bodyguards. However, under the leadership of Heinrich Himmler its power increased dramatically — especially after the Night of the Long Knives (see page 38). Its role expanded to cover the following issues:

- **Intelligence and security** were in the hands of the Gestapo led by **Reinhard Heydrich**. His agents could arrest people without trial and send them into the concentration camps. Fear of the Gestapo turned Germany into a nation of informers as people tried to protect themselves by incriminating others.
- The **military divisions**, known as the Waffen SS, were brutal but highly rated. In 1939 the SS had only three divisions, but during the war it expanded rapidly and fought alongside the traditional German army.

- **Race** could include all aspects of Nazi racial policy — extermination, slave labour and resettlement. The SS expanded the system of concentration camps (especially in eastern Europe) and some became extermination camps, e.g. Auschwitz run by the SS Death's Head Units (see Topic 7, page 75).

Figure 1 The structure of the SS

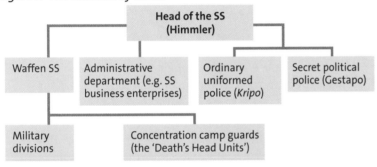

Heinrich Himmler, 1900–45

Despite his ordinary background and unremarkable character Himmler became leader of the SS from 1929 and Reichsführer SS, 1933–45. His influence grew and from 1942 he was, in effect, the second most powerful man in the Third Reich. His significance was:
- the expansion of the SS from 250 to 52,000 in the years 1929–33
- his responsibility for the purge in the Night of the Long Knives
- the development of a police state, which created a system of fear and control
- his obsessive racial policy, resulting in some of the most awful brutality and killings

The police and the courts

When the Nazis came to power they did not destroy the existing police forces and legal system. They took control of them gradually. As a result, the maintenance of general law and order (e.g. theft) remained the responsibility of the *Kripo*, but by 1939 it was under the control of Heydrich and the Gestapo.

At first, many judges were content to work with the Nazi regime, though over the years they felt the growing Nazi domination. In particular, judges were undermined by the creation of the Nazi new courts:
- The **Special Courts** to try political offences (e.g. listening to foreign radios stations) without a jury.
- The **People's Court** to try cases of high treason with a Nazi jury.

As a result, the increasing powers of the SS, especially in the war years, weakened the independence of the traditional German legal system fundamentally.

The party

The Nazi Party had been created and moulded in the 1920s to seize power, but after 1933 its actual role within Germany was never resolved. It became a large structure and it seemed to be highly organised (see Figure 2, on page 47). In reality, the party just consisted of many different uncoordinated groups, including the Hitler Youth (see Topic 6, page 61), the SA, Labour Front (see Topic 6, page 65) and *Gauleiters* — the local party leaders.

In fact, the planning of the party's organisations was poor. In addition, their work often clashed with the established German civil service (e.g. the judiciary and the foreign office).

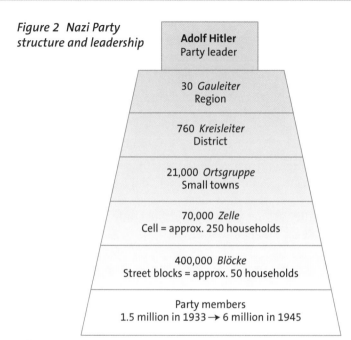

Figure 2 Nazi Party structure and leadership

| Adolf Hitler Party leader |
| 30 *Gauleiter* Region |
| 760 *Kreisleiter* District |
| 21,000 *Ortsgruppe* Small towns |
| 70,000 *Zelle* Cell = approx. 250 households |
| 400,000 *Blöcke* Street blocks = approx. 50 households |
| Party members 1.5 million in 1933 → 6 million in 1945 |

The German army

Traditionally, the army was a powerful organisation in Germany. It was conservative and had not been sympathetic to the Weimar Republic. Nonetheless, the army generals were suspicious of Nazism. As a result, Hitler needed to be careful not to alienate them (see Topic 4, page 38).

At first, the army was encouraged from 1933–38 because:

- It was excluded from the process of coordination in the first couple of years.
- It was relieved by the elimination of the SA.
- It was pleased by Hitler's foreign policy successes.

However, when some leading generals began to express concern about Nazi war plans in 1937–38, Hitler purged the army leadership. He removed the defence minister, the commander-in-chief and 16 other generals and replaced them with new appointments who supported his views.

Censorship and propaganda

 How did the Nazis use culture and the mass media to control the people?

Despite its power as a police state, it would have been difficult for Nazism to rule just by repression. It therefore wanted to control the Germans by means of **propaganda**. (Propaganda means the deliberate spreading of ideas and information to make people think and believe in a particular way.)

From the start, the Nazi propaganda machine was led and directed by **Joseph Goebbels**, the Minister of Popular Enlightenment and Propaganda. His aims were to:

- spread Nazi ideas, e.g. by portraying the Germans as a master race
- win over the support of the German people, e.g. by attacking the Jews and the communists for causing Germany's problems
- strengthen the Nazi regime, e.g. by promoting Hitler as a 'god-like' leader

Goebbels believed that the key to success was to keep the message simple and to keep repeating it.

All the means of public communication were brought under state control. For example:

- **The press**. Journalists and editors were closely censored by a state-controlled news agency, the **DNB**. Over the years the ownership of publications fell under the control of the Nazi publishing house, *Eher Verlag*.
- **Radio**. By 1934, all the nation's radio-broadcasting companies were brought under the control of the Reich Radio Company. Goebbels recognised the value of the radio and the 'people's receiver' was put into cheap mass production, so that by 1939, 70% of Germans had access to private radios. Loudspeakers were also placed in public places (television was only just being developed in the 1930s.)
- **Film**. Goebbels was fascinated by film. He saw it as new and dynamic. Newsreel and explicit propagandised films were produced. One of the most well known of these was the anti-Semitic documentary, *The Eternal Jew*, in which the Jews were depicted as carriers and spreaders of disease. However, Goebbels believed that propaganda succeeded best if people also enjoyed the cinema, so many general entertaining films were also produced.
- **Mass rallies** (e.g. the Nuremberg Rallies). The aim of these meetings was to create such a powerful emotional atmosphere that all members of the crowd would support Nazism as a mass movement. Every kind of device was used to heighten the effect: uniforms, torches, music, salutes, flags, songs and anthems, and the speeches from leading personalities.

A good example of the use of Nazi propaganda was the **Berlin Olympics of 1936**. Persecution of the Jews was suspended at the time and the Nazis were keen to portray their economic and sporting successes (though their image of the 'master-race' was undermined by the black American athlete, Jesse Owens, who won four gold medals).

Culture

All forms of culture were expected to conform to Nazi expectations. So, architects, painters and sculptors did not enjoy the artistic freedom to express their ideas and they faced **censorship** (in contrast to the Weimar years). They could only work under the control of the Reich Chamber of Culture.

Art

Many of the themes of modern art, such as anti-war and social change, were dismissed and seen as 'degenerate'. As a result, the works of leading artists, such as Picasso and Dix, were banned. In contrast, the Nazis were keen to encourage images showing the Romantic style of the German landscape with forests and mountains and heroic images of the master race.

Cinema

Some of the films produced are rated highly to this day. For example, the female director Leni Riefenstahl made the documentary films *Triumph of the Will* and *Olympia*. In addition, hundreds of 'entertainment' films were made. Their aim was to present the political message with more subtlety (e.g. *Kolberg*, an epic about Germany's opposition to Napoleon and *Jud Süss*, the story of an eighteenth-century Jew hanged for his crimes).

Architecture

The Bauhaus school of design, with its modern style — which had flourished in Weimar Germany — was disliked by the Nazis. Hitler himself encouraged the construction of large public buildings of stone with columns and steps similar to those in ancient Greece and Rome. These buildings would reflect the strength, power and importance of the state and the nation over individuals.

Music

Modern music was censored closely. Jazz music and the 'jitterbug' dance were not allowed, as both originated with 'racially inferior black Americans'. The works of classical German composers like Bach, Beethoven and Wagner were encouraged, as well as traditional folk music.

Persecution

 Why did the Nazis persecute many groups in German society?

The Nazis wanted to create a master race. They believed that the Germans were part of a people of northern Europe called the **Aryans** (see page 24). They saw themselves as superior in terms of mental and physical abilities and they saw other races, like the Jews and Slavs, as inferior.

The Nazis therefore aimed to maintain the purity of 'good blood' by controlling the breeding of desirable inherited (Aryan) features.

At the same time, the more undesirable 'sub-human' races, as well as people with mental and physical disabilities, were to be dealt with.

Nazi anti-Semitism

Anti-Semitism did not start with the Nazis — it goes back hundreds of years. However, it was an essential part of Hitler's thinking and he blamed the Jews for Germany's defeat in the First World War and the country's economic problems. Nazism therefore developed an extreme form of anti-Semitism. It used various methods against the Jews in the years 1933–39:

- **The boycott**. A one-day nationwide boycott of Jewish businesses and shops was organised for 1 April 1933, because of the influence of many radical Nazis. It was not universally implemented and the party's leaders were cautious. Nevertheless, it was the first real sign of Nazi anti-Semitism in action.
- **Propaganda**. Goebbels used the full range of propaganda methods to spread anti-Semitic messages including:
  – posters and speeches
  – newspapers, e.g. the violent and near pornographic weekly, **Der Stürmer**, edited by the *Gauleiter* Julius Streicher
  – films (see page 48)
- **Education**. The Nazis controlled the curriculum and textbooks to spread the anti-Jewish message (see Topic 6).
- **Racial laws**. Discrimination against the Jews got worse as the range of laws gradually increased (see Table 1 on page 50).

Table 1 Discrimination against Jews

7 April 1933	Exclusion of Jews from civil service.
Sep 1935	The Nuremberg Race Laws. Reich Citizenship Act (Jews lost their citizenship in Germany). Law for the Protection of German Honour and Blood (marriage and sexual relations between Jews and Aryans forbidden).
July 1938	Jewish doctors stopped from practising medicine.
Nov 1938	Expulsion of Jewish pupils from schools.
Dec 1938	Compulsory closure and sale of all Jewish businesses.
Sep 1939	German Jews placed under curfew.

- **Violence**. From the start many ordinary Nazis took advantage of their power to use violence against Jews, e.g. attacks on property and physical attacks. The events of 1938 were on a different scale, however. This was when Goebbels deliberately encouraged a pogrom against the Jews, because of the murder by a young Jew of a German embassy official. (Pogrom is an old word meaning an organised or encouraged massacre of innocent people.) The night of 9–10 November 1938 became known as the **Night of Broken Glass (*Kristallnacht*)**. One hundred Jews were killed and thousands were sent to concentration camps. Two hundred synagogues and 8,000 businesses were burnt.

- **Emigration**. Some Jews had left Germany throughout the 1930s. However, from 1939 the **Reich Central Office for Jewish Emigration** was set up to encourage many more to emigrate, though the rules forced them to leave with no possessions and no money.

It is hard to explain why there was so little opposition to the persecution of the Jews, but the following factors may have been significant:
- Anti-Semitism was established in Germany (and in many European countries) long before the Nazi dictatorship.
- Hitler and many other Nazi leaders were committed anti-Semites and tended to use Jews as scapegoats for Germany's problems.
- Nazi propaganda led more Germans to believe that the Jews were the cause of their problems.
- Nazi laws and the police system made it difficult to resist anti-Semitism.

By the start of the Second World War nearly half of Germany's Jewish population had voluntarily emigrated and left the country. Topic 7 considers the fate of the remaining half — along with many other Jews around Europe.

Minorities

Other groups were also persecuted in Nazi Germany:
- The term **asocial** was used for anyone whose behaviour was viewed by the Nazis as not acceptable or not useful. It therefore covered alcoholics, homosexuals, prostitutes and the work-shy — and many ended up in concentration camps.

- As early as July 1933 the Nazis made a law that allowed for the **compulsory sterilisation** of people with hereditary illnesses, such as schizophrenia. Over the 12 years of the Nazi period 350,000 people were sterilised.
- Nazi racial policy went further in 1939, when Hitler started the **euthanasia** programme named **Operation T4**. It arranged for the 'mercy killing' of mentally handicapped people, e.g. people with Down's Syndrome, at asylums by injection and gas. About 70,000 patients were killed in 1940–41, but this was then stopped because of the opposition of the Catholic Church.
- There were only about 25,000 gypsies in Germany, but they became increasingly persecuted because of their lifestyle and racial background. In 1938, Himmler issued a decree, '**The Struggle against the Gypsy Plague**'. This ordered for the registration of gypsies by racial terms. After the start of the war gypsies were put into camps and the murders began. From 1942 gypsies were sent to Auschwitz and a large proportion of Europe's gypsy population was exterminated — nearly 500,000.

🔑 Key question

How effectively did the Nazis control Germany in the years 1933–39?

The Nazis did control Germany effectively, though the reality was not always quite so straightforward. Hitler himself cleverly strengthened his political leadership and in stages removed his main rivals — the trade unions, the SA and the dissident generals. And it seems that he was genuinely popular and seen as a strong, successful leader. However, he headed an inefficient and disorganised government because of all the competing elements.

As a result, Nazi control of Germany was guaranteed by several other factors:
- The power of the SS increased significantly over the years. The extensive system of policing and security and the obsessive persecution of the Jews and other minorities created an atmosphere of fear that kept the German people quiet. As a result, significant opposition did not threaten the regime until 1942 (see Topic 7, page 76).
- Goebbels's propaganda machine managed to establish total control over the public communication of news and ideas. It was therefore generally effective in censoring undesired material. It also effectively promoted such things as German nationalism and the 'Hitler myth'. However, it is doubtful whether Nazi propaganda challenged many Germans with well-established attitudes, such as Catholics and trade unionists.

Use the information on pages 45–51, your class notes and textbooks to answer the following questions.

1 Define and explain what is meant by the following terms:
a totalitarian
b censorship
c *Kristallnacht*
d Operation T4
e Reich Chamber of Culture

2 What were the three main functions of the SS in the period after 1934?

1a

b

c

d

e

2

Questions

3 a Give three factors for the basis of Hitler's political power.

3a
....
....
....

b Explain three of Hitler's political limitations.

b
....
....
....
....
....
....

4 Explain how each of the following helped Hitler to rule Nazi Germany:
a the Gestapo
b the party
c the army
d the police and the courts

4a
....
....
....

b
....
....

c
....
....

d
....
....

Source A

CORBIS

Photo of Hitler at a mass rally in Nuremberg, 1934

5

5 How useful is the photo in Source A as evidence of what life was like in Nazi Germany in the mid-1930s? Make sure you that you consider both the usefulness and limitations of this photo.

Questions

Source B

All Germany's radio stations were under Goebbels's control. He encouraged people to listen to the radio by producing cheap sets which most could afford. To make sure they could hear the radio when they were not at home, he had loudspeaker pillars built in the streets, and ordered all cafes to have their radios turned on for important programmes.

J. Brooman, *Hitler's Germany*, 1985

6 a Explain what you can learn from Source B about how the Nazis tried to control German society.

b From Source B and your own knowledge give reasons to explain why Goebbels took control of Germany's radio stations.

7 Complete the table to describe how the Nazis attempted to control German culture in the 1930s.

6a

b

7

Aspects of culture	What kind of cultural features did the Reich encourage?	What kind of cultural features did the Reich oppose?
Art	Traditional Romantic art, e.g. landscapes	
Architecture		
Music		

8 All books, films and paintings were subject to censorship by the Nazis. Study the text on pages 48–49 and then search the internet to find out the information to complete the table.

8

Name of artist	Type of work	Censored or celebrated by the Nazis?	Reasons why
E. M. von Remarque			Pacifist who wrote *All Quiet on the Western Front*
Leni Riefenstahl			
Otto Dix			
Albert Speer			
Bertolt Brecht		Censored	
Arno Breker			
Walter Gropius	Architect/designer		
Pablo Picasso			
Ludwig van Beethoven		Celebrated	

9 Study the beliefs and values in the table. State whether each one was supported or opposed by Nazi culture.

9

Patriotism		**Aryan supremacy**	
Pacifism		**Press freedom**	
Communism	Opposed	**Christianity**	
Democracy		**Anti-Semitism**	Supported
Leadership		**Militarism**	

Questions

10 Explain why the Nazis persecuted the Jews.

11 Complete the chart by listing the following events in the correct chronological order and explaining their significance.

- German Jews placed under curfew
- Compulsory closure and sale of all Jewish businesses
- Night of Broken Glass
- Nuremberg Race Laws
- First boycott of Jewish shops and businesses
- Creation of the Reich Central Office for Jewish Emigration
- Berlin Olympic Games
- Exclusion of Jews from civil service

11

Date	Event	Significance
1 April 1933		
	Exclusion of Jews from civil service	

Sources C and D refer to the attacks on Jewish property known as 'Kristallnacht' or the 'Night of Broken Glass', 9–10 November 1938.

Source C

It was a spontaneous wave of anger throughout Germany as a result of the cowardly murder of third Secretary von Rath in the German Embassy in Paris.

Nazi press statement of 10 November 1938

Source D

The damage was done by SS men and Stormtroopers not in uniform, each group having been provided with hammers, axes, crowbars and incendiary bombs.

An American observer, November 1938

12 a In what ways is the content of Sources C and D different?

b Explain possible reasons why these interpretations are different. Use both sources and your own knowledge to explain your answer.

13 Give three additional examples of minority groups persecuted by the Nazis. Explain why the Nazis persecuted each of these groups.

Extended writing

On separate paper, write a short essay in answer to the following question.

14 'The most important factor enabling the Nazis to control German people was their use of propaganda.' Do you agree with this view?

12a

b

13

Topic 6 Life in Nazi Germany, 1933–39

 Key question

To what extent did the German people benefit from Nazi rule in the 1930s?

 Key content

- Women and the family
- Youth and education
- The churches and religion
- The economy

Women and the family

? How successful were Nazi policies towards women and the family?

Nazi thinking was in contrast to that of the Weimar years, when there had been a move towards offering women equal opportunities. The Nazis believed that a woman's place was in the home and they supported the traditional German vision of the **three Ks — *Kinder, Küche, Kirche*** ('Children, Kitchen and Church').

A woman's role in Nazi Germany was to:
- produce babies and bring up the children
- care for the home and their husbands
- stay at home

Work versus home

Nazism attacked the 'working woman' from the start. This was because it was seen as 'natural' for the man to be the worker and the provider. Moreover, the Depression in the early 1930s coincided with the argument to remove women from the workplace in an attempt to reduce the high unemployment.

As a result, the Nazis soon introduced policies such as:
- reducing the number of women in professional jobs, e.g. medicine, teaching and law
- limiting women joining university to 10%
- banning female lawyers and judges

Mothers and children

In addition, the Nazis' aim to support a woman's place in the home was directly connected with its motive to increase the national population. This was partly because the birth rate was declining (many had died in the First World War), but also to provide more young soldiers to strengthen the Third Reich.

The main financial incentives provided were:
- **marriage loans** for women who gave up their jobs — and a quarter of the repayment on those loans was cancelled for each child born
- **family allowances** for low-paid workers and **tax allowances for children**

Nazi propaganda also launched campaigns to enhance the status of wives and mothers through the introduction of the

Mother's Cross for large families. In addition, abortion was not allowed and contraception facilities were limited.

The Nazis not only wanted more births, but also 'healthy' and 'racially sound' children. Maternity services and childcare facilities were improved quite significantly. However, there was a strong racial element to Nazi female welfare:

- The **sterilisation policy** (see Topic 5, page 51) was aimed at preventing mentally and physically disabled women from having more children.
- The **Marriage Law of 1935** only allowed couples to marry with proof of racial and medical purity.
- The **Lebensborn** ('Spring of Life') programme provided homes for the increasing number of illegitimate children who were seen as racially correct. (Later, the homes became facilities for SS officers to father children.)

Impact

The effects of Nazi policy on women and the family are not clear. In several ways the Nazis could claim partial success:

- the birth rate rose between 1933 and 1939 (but fell after 1939)
- the marriage rate increased at first (but levelled off from 1935)
- the financial loans and welfare services for married women and children were generous
- the percentage of women in jobs fell from 37% to 31% of the total from 1932 to 1937, at which point it began to rise again

Despite Nazi aims and policies, it was actually the government's demands of rearmament which influenced the position of women from 1937. The shortage of labour drew more and more women away from the home and towards the workplace — a tendency that increased when the war started (see Topic 7, page 74).

It is even more difficult to assess women's attitudes to Nazism. On one level, some women (often many with professional careers) felt that the Nazis were hostile to women. For example, the only female involvement allowed in the party was in the women's organisations, like the DFW.

However, Nazi sympathisers would not have said that women were discriminated against, but were simply treated in a different way. They saw women's role as restoring their traditional status and position in the home and the community.

Youth and education

 How successful were Nazi policies for young people?

Hitler and the Nazis aimed to create the Third Reich to last for 1,000 years. They wanted to 'shape' Germany's younger generations to be loyal and committed to Nazism by:

- controlling and disciplining the youth
- indoctrinating the youth with Nazi principles (boys were to be prepared for military training and girls for motherhood)

These aims were to be achieved through the youth movements and the education system.

Schools

The German education system was well established and its

schools had a reputation for high standards. However, the Nazis were determined to change the schools by:

- taking control away from regional governments and giving it to the Ministry of Education
- pressurising teachers to join the Nazi Teachers' League and retraining them through courses (Jews were banned from the profession)

As a result, the teaching of subjects was changed in various ways:

- History concentrated on topics with pro-nationalist and anti-democratic views, e.g. the rise of Nazism, the unfairness of the Treaty of Versailles and the evils of communism.
- Biology taught about racial theories and the need to keep the population pure.
- Sport/PE was given 15% of school time. The emphasis of the physical over the academic was to prepare boys as soldiers and girls as healthy mothers.
- Religious studies became less important and by 1937 pupils were allowed to drop the subject.
- Girls also had to study domestic science, including health studies about their role in Nazi society.

Generally, teachers were encouraged to promote Nazi ideas at all times — for example, Jewish children were often mocked in classes.

In addition, elite schools were created to prepare boys for future political and military leadership — 21 Napolas, 10 Adolf Hitler Schools and 3 Ordensburgen.

The Hitler Youth (HJ)

The Nazis wanted to take the control of children away from family, school and church. Therefore, they believed that the Hitler Youth was vital because it could be completely run by the party and indoctrinate the children exactly as they wanted.

Under the leadership of **Baldur von Schirach**, the Hitler Youth movement expanded enormously from 1933. It was organised into four sections and by 1939 it had become compulsory (see Table 1).

Table 1 Hitler Youth (HJ)

Boys	10–14 years old	DJ, the German Young People
Boys	14–18 years old	HJ, the Hitler Youth
Girls	10–14 years old	JM, the League of Young Girls
Girls	14–18 years old	BDM, the League of German Girls

The Hitler Youth certainly tried to indoctrinate the youngsters through political talks, though it concentrated more on the physical and practical side of education. This was usually arranged at regular local meetings, but the Nazi leadership was keen to organise camping trips, which took the youngsters away from home for more concentrated indoctrination. The camps put great emphasis on sports and activities for both boys and girls, such as hiking and athletics. It was only the boys who participated in military tasks, like shooting, while the girls were made to do gymnastics and dance.

All of these activities tried to develop Nazi values, such as commitment, discipline, hard work, patriotism and the importance of the family.

Impact

It is difficult to measure how successful was Nazi indoctrination of German youth. In one sense, Nazi education policy was successful: the regime managed to exert a strict control over Germany's young people and the Hitler Youth membership increased to nearly 8 million by 1938. There were also many positive features, such as the range of physical activities, the camping and music, which were enjoyed by (and even inspired) many youngsters — especially if they came from poor backgrounds and had never travelled before.

However, it should be remembered that from the start youngsters were strongly encouraged to join the Hitler Youth by the party and in 1939 membership was made **compulsory**. Later evidence also suggests that some youngsters, after the initial enthusiasm, became more cynical and refused to accept all the discipline and the ideology lectures. By the time of the onset of the war, opposition youth groups had started to emerge (see Topic 7, page 76).

Ironically, Nazi educational aims also enjoyed success because of the increased emphasis on the physical over the academic. However, there were unplanned consequences — the status of academic subjects declined along with educational standards. The number of students enrolling for university fell significantly and during the war there were shortages of people trained in the technical subjects required for war production.

Churches and religion

 How effectively did the Nazis change religious life in Germany?

In some ways the Christian Churches sympathised with Nazism because:
- They were more frightened by the threat of communism, which was anti-religious.
- They supported traditional values, especially the importance of the family.
- They resented the decadent reputation of Weimar Germany (see Topic 2, page 19).

However, Nazi leaders despised Christian values. They hoped to control the Christian Churches and to replace them with the German Faith Movement — a new pagan faith with ancient rituals.

The Roman Catholic Church

The relationship between Catholicism and the Nazi regime was complex. This was partly because German Catholics were part of an international church, but also because they had been persecuted back in nineteenth-century Germany. Nevertheless, in July 1933, the Nazi government and the Vatican signed an agreement, called a **concordat**. By its terms the Pope promised that the Church and its priests would stay out of politics; in response Hitler promised not to interfere in Church affairs, especially Catholic schools.

However, differences quickly emerged. The Nazis did not keep to the agreement and growing Catholic concerns led to the papal statement from Pius XI in 1937, '**Mit Brennender Sorge**' ('With Burning Anxiety'). By the late 1930s the Church's schools and youth movements were being continually harassed.

The Protestant Churches

The Nazi regime hoped to control the Protestant Churches by creating the German Christian Church under the pro-Nazi Ludwig Müller, who became Reich Bishop. His supporters became known as the German Christians and they used Nazi style uniforms and salutes.

However, many pastors were hostile to the German Christians and instead, nearly half of them formed the Confessional Church, led by **Martin Niemöller**. From that time the Nazis placed increasing restrictions on the uncooperative pastors. For example, Niemöller himself was imprisoned from 1937 in a concentration camp because of his highly critical sermons about Nazism's religious policy and anti-Semitism.

The impact

The Nazis did not succeed in changing religious life in Germany. This was for several reasons. First, the German Faith Movement was a failure. It attracted officially only 5% of the population. Second, most Germans remained loyal to their Christian faith and the Protestant and Catholic Churches survived in the long term, despite the attacks of Nazism. Third, many individual churchmen showed great bravery — 8,000 out of 17,000 pastors were arrested and about 40% of the Catholic clergy were harassed.

On the other hand, Nazism remained politically strong until the end of the war. Therefore, it could be said that Protestantism and Roman Catholicism also failed because they did not effectively resist Nazism and tended to concentrate on their own institutions.

The Nazi economy

 How successful were Nazi economic policies?

Aims

The Depression had hit Germany particularly badly (see Topic 3, pages 26–27). By 1933 its major economic problems were:
- **Mass unemployment**. Trade had collapsed and this led to 6.1 million unemployed.
- **Industrial production** had declined by 40%.
- **Deflation**. Prices and wages were falling (unlike the inflation of 1923). Deflation made it hard for businesses and farmers to make enough profits to keep going.

The Nazis had to deal with the economic crisis, otherwise, they faced little chance of keeping the people's support.

In power, the main aims of the Nazis were to:
- create jobs and reduce unemployment
- build up the German armaments industry and strengthen the German armed forces
- make Germany more economically self-sufficient; this policy (known as **autarky**) was to reduce Germany's dependence on expensive imports, especially if it was blockaded in a war

Recovery, 1933–36

In the early years the German economy was in the hands of the financial genius **Hjalmar Schacht**, Minister of Economy, 1934–37. He set out to solve Germany's problems in the following ways:

- **Government spending**. A large programme of public works was set up to create jobs, e.g. autobahnen (motorways), houses, government buildings and forestry conservation. Some of the work was done by the RAD (National Labour Service) which was introduced for all 18–25 year olds.
- **Rearmament**. Hitler allowed the start of rearmament, which stimulated the heavy industries, e.g. coal, iron and steel. In addition, conscription was introduced in 1935. This both strengthened the armed forces and reduced the number of unemployed people.
- **Trade agreements**. The German government tried to control trade by making deals with countries in eastern Europe. This allowed the government to exchange food and raw materials for industrial products.

By the end of 1936 the Nazi economy was recovering. Schacht was actually worried that the economy was growing too fast and he wanted to reduce arms spending. However, Hitler said that 'the German economy must be fit for war within 4 years', so he argued for increased arms expenditure. These differences led to a crisis in autumn 1936 and a fundamental change in economic policy. Göring was put in charge of the Four-Year Plan, while Schacht's influence declined and in 1937 he resigned.

The Four-Year Plan

The key aim of the **Four-Year Plan** was to make Germany ready for war by making it more self-sufficient under the policy of **autarky**. Above all, it wanted to avoid repeating the effects of the British naval blockade in the First World War, when Germany was 'starved' of the food and materials it needed.

The objectives of the Four-Year Plan were to:
- reduce imports
- increase production of raw materials, e.g. coal, iron
- develop synthetic materials because of shortages, e.g. oil and rubber
- increase agricultural production

Hermann Göring, 1893–1946

Göring joined the Nazis early and was injured when he took part in the Munich Putsch. He could be charming and witty, but was also brutal and greedy — he made a massive personal fortune. During 1933–34 he organised the German police, the SA and SS, and used violence and terror to secure Nazi power. He was deeply involved in the Reichstag Fire (see page 37) and the Night of the Long Knives (see pages 38–39).

From 1936 he became in effect the economic dictator of Nazi Germany and was politically close to Hitler. However, after the military failure of the Luftwaffe to win the Battle of Britain, his influence declined.

In the late 1930s the Nazi regime poured in billions of Reichs-marks and there was a strong economic boom. However, Göring's slogan, 'Guns make us powerful. Butter only makes us fat', shows clearly that Nazi Germany was set on a war of conquest.

Economic effects

The Nazis succeeded in restoring some hope after the Great Depression and the German economy made a remarkable recovery:

- Unemployment fell from 6 million in 1933 to 1.6 million by 1936, and by 1939 there was a shortage of workers.
- Public works, like the motorways and public buildings, restored a sense of national pride.
- The Nazis directed the economy by controlling wages, prices and imports (and, of course, by establishing industrial peace and no strikes).

However, it should be remembered that:

- From the start Nazi Germany was overspending. It could only solve the problem of its debts by conquering other countries.
- The autarky policy therefore had only limited success — Germany still depended on one third of foreign imports for its required raw materials.
- When the war did start in 1939, the Germany economy was not ready.

Social effects

Nazi economic policy had different consequences for different social groups.

Industrial workers

The creation of new jobs was the most obvious benefit for many of the long-term unemployed German workers. Indeed, by the late 1930s there was a labour shortage. Moreover, workers were attracted by the various initiatives of the DAF (German Labour Front) under the leadership of Robert Ley:

- **KdF (*Kraft durch Freude*)**, 'Strength through Joy', provided benefits, such as holidays, sports and cultural activities.
- The organisation **SdA (*Schönheit der Arbeit*)**, 'Beauty of Labour', supervised working conditions such as meals and cleaning.
- Cheap flats were made available.

However, strikes were declared illegal and workers lost their rights. Working hours and wages were also closely controlled. Moreover, 'real wages' did not increase significantly. So the pressures probably increased workers' discontent and grumbling by 1939.

Farmers/peasantry

The Nazis were keen to satisfy the farming community, who had suffered badly from the Depression. As a result, they cancelled debts on farms and introduced the **Reich Entailed Farm Law**. This encouraged small farms with the use of tax allowances and low interest rates. The **Reich Food Estate** was also created with a central board to buy and distribute all agricultural produce.

As a result, agricultural production and prices increased in the 1930s (but from a very low level). However, there was still considerable peasant discontent — and significantly, youngsters drifted to the town from the countryside.

Middle classes

It is difficult to generalise about the fortunes of the shopkeepers and small businesses. Many were at first sympathetic to the Nazis and were grateful to them for dealing with the threat of communism. However, they did not thrive because they faced much stiffer competition from the larger businesses. The number of small-employed craftsmen also continued to fall.

Engineering firms did better than manufacturers of consumer goods.

Big business

Those who gained most were the owners of big companies, especially those involved in the armaments industries. Certainly, the Nazi government increased its control over big business, but it enjoyed clear advantages:

- Trade unions were weakened and wages were controlled.
- Major contracts were given by the government.

As a result, in the 1930s the large firms benefited from a rapid economic expansion and profits were good.

 Key question

To what extent did the German people benefit from Nazi rule in the 1930s?

It is difficult to generalise about the benefits of Nazi rule in the years up to 1939, but you need to consider *how* the following factors would have influenced the lives of individual Germans under Nazi rule:

- social class — industrial workers, farmers, middle classes and big business
- gender — different roles of men and women
- religion — Jews, Jehovah Witnesses, Catholics and Protestants
- age — youth organisations and schools

It is also important to bear in mind these general factors affecting German people:

- changing economic conditions
- foreign policy successes
- political stability and security (but with the cost of severe repression)

Questions

Use the information on pages 59–66, your class notes and textbooks to answer the following questions.

1 Give three ways that the Nazis tried to encourage women to increase the German population.

2 What can you learn from Source A about the role women were expected to play in Nazi Germany?

Source A

Illustration from a Nazi textbook.

MARY EVANS/WEIMAR ARCHIVE

1

2

Questions

Topic 6 Life in Nazi Germany, 1933–39

3 Complete the table about the success of Nazi aims for women.

Nazi aims	Successes	Failures
Employment		
Population		

4 The Nazis changed many of the school subjects. Choose two of them and explain why.

5 a What was the overall aim of the Hitler Youth?

b What values did the Hitler Youth try to develop?

c Briefly describe the main kind activities of the Hitler Youth.

Questions

6 Explain what you can learn from Source B (and your own knowledge) about how the Nazis controlled education.

7 Study Source C. Why was this illustration printed in a children's book in the 1930s? In your answer make certain that you explain the Nazis' purpose in publishing the book at that time. Use the source and your own knowledge to develop your answer.

6

7

Source C

WIENER LIBRARY ARCHIVE

Illustration from a Nazi textbook

Source D

To keep a mentally ill person costs approximately 4 RM per day, and there are 300,000 mentally ill in care.

(i) How much do these people cost to keep in total?

(ii) How many marriage loans at 1000 RM could be granted from this money?

Source E

Life in the camp appeared to be one of healthy exercise in sports and games, but absolute discipline was maintained. By this I do not mean it was harshly enforced. The boys were happy to accept it.

It seemed to me also that, although every boy was conscious of his approaching military service, there was little if any drill performed in the camp. The leader had, of course, served in the German army, and military enthusiasm is part of the healthy and cheerful pattern of the German Boy Scout movement.

C. W. Domville-Fife, *This is Germany*, a British writer, 1939

Source F

It is claimed that the work of the Hitler Youth is in no way a pre-military training. All the same, I should think it a good preparation for the army. The children learn discipline. They march in ranks. They drill. When I attended a Hitler Youth camp, I asked a boy what they had done last night. In the presence of several others and one of the leaders, he said pistol shooting. Very good fun, and not necessarily a military pastime. However, it hardly justifies the claim that the youth movements have nothing to do with military training.

J. A. Cole, *Just Back from Germany*, a British writer, 1938

8 Source D contains maths questions from a textbook produced in Germany in the 1930s. How useful is this source to a historian studying Nazi attitudes to mentally disabled people?

9 In what ways is the content of Sources E and F different? Make sure that you provide a comparison of the sources explaining clearly the differences between the two sources.

8

9

Questions

10 How successful were the Nazis at influencing German youth? Give some of their successes and failures.

10 Successes	Failures

11 a In what ways did the Nazis attempt to control the activities of the Churches in the 1930s? Describe at least three examples.

b Did the Nazis really change religious life in Germany?

11a

b

12 Define and explain what is meant by the following economic terms:
a deflation
b autarky
c labour shortages
d interest rates

12a

b

c

d

13 a List three ways in which the Nazis reduced German unemployment.

13a

b Explain how these factors helped the Germans economy to recover between 1933 and 1936.

b

14 a What was the main aim of the Four-Year Plan?

14a

b What were its objectives from 1936?

b

Source G

Unemployment and production in Germany	1928	1930	1932	1934	1936	1938
Unemployment (millions)	1.4	3.1	5.6	2.7	1.6	0.4
Industrial production (1928 =100)	100	87	58	83	107	125

Figure adapted from G. Layton, *The Third Reich*

15 How useful is Source G to a historian studying the recovery of the German economy in the 1930s?

15

Questions

16 Complete the table to show how the Nazi economy affected people in Germany in the 1930s.

16	Social group	Benefits	Drawbacks
	Industrial workers		
	Farmers/peasantry		
	Middle classes		
	Big business		

Extended writing

On separate paper, write a short essay in answer to the following question.

17 How far did the German people benefit from Nazi rule in the 1930s?

Topic 7 Impact of the war, 1939–45

 Key question

What was the impact of the Second World War on Germany?

 Key content

- The war economy
- The Holocaust
- Opposition

The war economy, 1939–45

 How did the war change life in Germany?

In the early war years of 1939–41 Germany was incredibly successful and its military victories gave the impression of economic strength.

However, the Nazi economy was not properly prepared, as Hitler had not planned on a world war starting in 1939. As a result, from the earliest days of the war, the Nazis needed to introduce rationing of food, clothes and basic items, such as soap and toilet paper. At the same time, ironically, some luxuries seemed to be more available because they were sold on the black market from the conquered countries.

By 1942 Germany found itself at war with Britain, Russia and the USA. It faced a long drawn-out conflict. As a result,

under the leadership of **Albert Speer**, the Minister of Armaments, the German economy was made to fight a 'total war'. This meant that every part of German society was geared to the war effort:

- Industry was organised more efficiently.
- Working hours were increased.
- More women were drafted into work.
- Even millions of foreign workers were encouraged to work (but under controls).
- Non-essential businesses were closed.

War production increased dramatically and reached a peak in the summer of 1944. However, the war had increasingly severe consequences on the German people:

- Food rationing increasingly led to real shortages.
- Clothes rationing was ended because clothes were not made any longer.
- Bombing of the industrial cities, e.g. Hamburg and Berlin, killed thousands of civilians.
- Production of magazines and sweets was stopped.

Table 1 Bombs dropped on Germany and Britain, 1940–44

Date	On Germany	On Britain
1940	10, 000	36,844
1942	40,000	3,265
1944	650,000	9,151

Despite these efforts, the German economy was just not strong enough to win the war because:

- Allied resources and labour were far superior to Germany's.
- From 1943 Germany began to lose control of the conquered lands and raw materials.
- Allied bombing in the cities hindered industrial production.

By spring 1945 Germany was in ruins.

The Holocaust

 How was it possible for the Nazis to carry out mass murder?

The onset of the Second World War marked a turning point in the Nazi treatment of the Jews (see also Topic 5). The series of Nazi military victories in 1939–41 meant that millions of Jews in Europe were now under the control of the Nazis, especially in Poland and Russia. In addition, emigration for Jews to independent countries became even more difficult.

To deal with their 'Jewish problem' the Nazis resorted to ever more extreme measures:

- In Poland, Jews in towns were forced to live in **ghettos** in appalling living conditions.
- All Jews were forced to wear the **Star of David**.
- When Russia was invaded in 1941 the German army was supported by the **SS Einsatzgruppen** — four special 'Action Units' responsible for rounding up local Jews and murdering them by mass shootings and then using mass graves to bury them. By the end of that year it is estimated that this bloody process had killed 700,000 Jews, but it showed the practical difficulty for the Nazis of killing so many people.

The Nazi leaders decided on a 'final solution' to the Jews — to exterminate all of them. There remains uncertainty over when exactly it was decided to commit genocide on the Jews. It was being considered during 1941. However, it was not formally agreed until the **Wannsee Conference** organised by Heydrich and Himmler on 20 January 1942. As a result of the conference, it was agreed to build extermination camps to gas Europe's 11 million Jews.

In the next 3 years about 6 million Jews from all over Europe were murdered at the notorious camps in Poland, including Auschwitz and Sobibor. This episode in history has become known as the **Holocaust** (meaning 'sacrifice'). It should not be forgotten that the Nazis also carried out genocide against the people of several other minorities, most notably the gypsies and Jehovah Witnesses.

The Holocaust has been described as 'the most horrible crime ever committed in the whole history of the world'. Yet, it is still difficult to explain satisfactorily why human beings resorted to such behaviour.

In political terms:

- By 1942 most of Europe was under the control of the Nazis.
- Nazi Germany was a totalitarian and brutal regime and its leadership had made the big decisions.

In practical terms:

- The Nazis had the technical means to organise 'industrial death' by applying the gas.
- Nazi Germany had an extensive train system to transport millions of people.

- The extermination camps were created and run in a high degree of secrecy.

In human terms:
- Many thousands of Germans (and other nationalities) cooperated simply because they were 'obeying orders'.
- War brutalised people's behaviour.
- Some Nazis strongly believed the ideology of racism and anti-Semitism.

Opposition to the Nazis

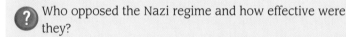

Who opposed the Nazi regime and how effective were they?

Although there were people who criticised Hitler and the Nazis, significant opposition did not really emerge until 1942.

Communists

The Communist Party was quickly repressed during 1933, but many groups carried on as part of an underground movement. They printed pamphlets and tried to encourage strikes and some even carried out acts of sabotage. The most successful was the spy network called the **Red Orchestra**. This passed information to Soviet Russia between 1938 and 1942.

Students

Hans and Sophie Scholl were students during the war at the University of Munich. By 1942 they were so upset about the war and the reports of massacres on the Eastern Front that they

formed a group called the **White Rose**. As a result they produced and distributed leaflets criticising the moral failure of the Nazis.

In February 1943 a more open demonstration led to their arrest and execution by the Gestapo.

Conservatives

There had always been some conservatives (aristocrats, generals and intellectuals) who had disliked Nazism, but opposition did not really come to a head until the winter of 1942–43. The leading group was the **Kreisau Circle**, which held secret meetings to draw up the 'Basic Principles of the New Order' and the plans for a new democratic government.

However, some of its members wanted to do more than talk. Colonel Stauffenberg believed that Nazism was leading to disaster and his aim was to assassinate Hitler and replace the Nazi government. On 20 July 1944 he planted a bomb close to Hitler at a meeting, but Hitler survived with injuries and the cost of failure was expensive: 5,000 conspirators were executed.

Youth

Even before 1939 some young people had not conformed to the behaviour expected of the Nazis (see Topic 6, page 62).

As the war years went on, opposition from some youngsters began to emerge. The **Edelweiss Pirates** represented a range of working-class gangs (e.g. Roving Dudes and the Navajos). And the **Swing Youth** was like a 'craze' among the middle class in clubs which deliberately encouraged jazz and swing music from the USA and Great Britain.

These groups were never organised, but from 1942 some started to produce anti-war leaflets and write graffiti on walls. Most famously, 12 Edelweiss Pirates were hanged publicly in 1944.

 Key question

What was the impact of the Second World War on Germany?

Table 2 Impact of Second World War on Germany

Military phases	Developments in Germany
1939–41 **The years of** **Nazi victories**	▪ Introduction of food/clothes rationing. Casualties limited. ▪ Luxuries imported from conquered lands.
1941–43 **The 'turn of** **the tide'**	▪ 'Final solution' started to exterminate Jews. Speer's reforms to mobilise the war economy. ▪ Creation of the Kreisau Circle. ▪ White Rose group of students at Munich.
1943–44 **'Total war'**	▪ Goebbels's speech rallied the people for a 'total war'. ▪ Allied mass bombing of Germany, e.g. Hamburg fire-storm. ▪ Manufacture of clothes ended and clothes rationing suspended. ▪ Stauffenberg's 'July plot' failed.
1944–45 **Defeat**	▪ Auschwitz liberated by the USSR. ▪ Food only available on black market. ▪ Dresden bombing — thousands killed in two nights by the Allies. ▪ Hitler's suicide in Berlin.

Questions

Use the information on pages 74–77, your class notes and your textbooks to answer the following questions.

1 Give three explanations for how the Minister of Armaments, Albert Speer, improved the German war economy from 1942.

2 Describe and explain some of the human consequences of the war in Germany:
a housing
b food
c working conditions

3 Explain how and why the following dates were turning points in the persecution of the Jews by the Nazis:
a 1 September 1939
b 22 June 1942
c 20 January 1942

4 Give four factors that help to explain why the Holocaust happened.

1

2a

b

c

3a

b

c

4

Questions

Source A

Number of German, British, US and Soviet tanks produced, 1940–45

Tank production	Germany	Britain	USA	USSR
1940	1,600	1,400	300	2,800
1942	6,300	8,600	25,000	24,700
1944	19,000	4,600	17,600	29,000
1945	3,900	N/A	12,000	15,400

Source B

A photo of the German city of Cologne after the Thousand-Bomb Raid on 30 May 1942

5 a Explain what you can learn from Source A about the German economy during the war.

5a

b Although the German economy continued to grow until 1944, why did Germany lose the war? Use Sources A and B and your own knowledge to answer the question.

b

Source C

A large section of the nation cannot imagine how the war will end and the telling of vulgar jokes against the state, even about the Führer himself, has increased considerably since Stalingrad.

A report of the intelligence bureau of the SD (a section of the Gestapo) produced in 1943

Source D

I feel a growing sense of wild vitality within myself, and of sorrow too. Is that what the British are trying to achieve by attacking civilians? At any rate they are not softening us up...The disaster which hits the Nazis and anti-Nazis alike is welding the people together.

A comment in February 1944 in the diary of Ursula Kardorff, a journalist

6 a Read Sources C and D about German morale during the war. Provide a comparison of the two sources detecting any similarities and differences.

6a

....

....

....

....

....

....

b How useful is Source C as evidence to a historian studying German morale during the war?

b

....

....

....

Extended writing

On separate paper, write a short essay in answer to the following question.

....

....

7 Why did the German resistance not destroy the Nazi dictatorship?

....